WOMEN'S
NEW
GOSPEL QUARTETS

By IRA B. WILSON

Cantare
Servire
Est

One Dollar per copy

50 Walker St.
New York 13

LORENZ
PUBLISHING CO.

209 S. State St.
Chicago 4

501 E. Third St.
Dayton 1, Ohio

Printed in U.S.A.

INDEX

(Women's New Gospel Quartets)

Women's New Gospel Quartets.

1.

Praise Ye the Lord.

W. C. Poole.

E. S. Lorenz.

1. For count-less bless-ings day by day Praise ye the Lord!
2. For sum-mer flow-ers blooming fair Praise ye the Lord!
3. For all his gifts of grace and love Praise ye the Lord!

For light that bright-ens all my way Praise ye the Lord!
For sweet-est songs and fra-grant air Praise ye the Lord!
Send up your praise to him a-bove, Praise ye the Lord!

CHORUS.

Praise him with gladness, praise him with song, Praise him who triumphs o'er sin and wrong;

Lift up your voices thro' all your days, Give God the glo-ry, give him the praise.

2. Jesus is the Friend You Need.

Geo. O. Webster.　　　　　　　　　　　　　　　　Ira B. Wilson.

1. When the days are dark and drear - y, Or life's bur-dens　press;
2. When the thorns so oft pre-vail - ing Cause your feet to　bleed,
3. Are life's per-ils thick a - round you, Near to him a - bide;
4. Je - sus will for-sake you nev - er, If his grace you　plead;

When the heart is torn and wea - ry With its sore dis - tress,
Je - sus is a Friend un - fail - ing, Just the Friend you　need.
For no e - vil can con-found you, Walk-ing by his　side.
Faith-ful to his prom - ise ev - er, Just the Friend you　need.

CHORUS.

Je - - sus is the Friend you need, Je - - sus is the
Je - sus is the Friend you need, Je - sus is the

Friend you need, Oth - er friends, tho' ten - der, kind, None like

Je - sus you can find, Je - sus is the Friend you need.

3. Savior, While My Heart is Tender.

John Burton. Herm. von Berge.

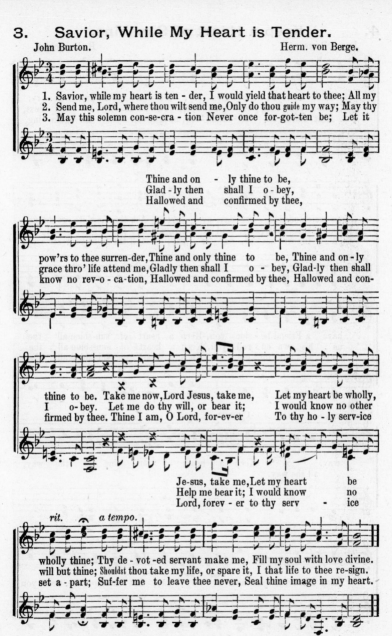

1. Savior, while my heart is ten - der, I would yield that heart to thee; All my pow'rs to thee surren-der, Thine and only thine to be, Thine and on - ly thine to be. Take me now, Lord Jesus, take me, Let my heart be wholly, wholly thine; Thy de - vot -ed servant make me, Fill my soul with love divine.

2. Send me, Lord, where thou wilt send me, Only do thou guide my way; May thy grace thro' life attend me, Gladly then shall I o - bey, Glad-ly then shall I o-bey. Let me do thy will, or bear it; I would know no other Help me bear it; I would know no will but thine; Shouldst thou take my life, or spare it, I that life to thee re-sign.

3. May this solemn con-se-cra - tion Never once for-got-ten be; Let it know no rev-o - ca-tion, Hallowed and confirmed by thee, Hallowed and con-firmed by thee. Thine I am, O Lord, for-ev-er To thy ho - ly serv-ice Lord, forev - er to thy serv - ice set a - part; Suf-fer me to leave thee never, Seal thine image in my heart.

rit. a tempo.

5

4. Keep a Heart of Sunshine.

James Rowe.   B. D. Ackley.

1. Life to you is drea - ry, oft - en you are wea - ry,
2. Tho' you long for glad - ness, you have on - ly sad - ness,
3. Lost in sin re - main - ing, naught can you be gain - ing,

Skies are clouded o - ver day by day; Ask the Lord to guide you,
Darkness keeps your wea - ry soul a - stray; Let the Lord con - trol you,
Such a life will nev - er, nev - er pay; Tell the Lord your sto - ry,

have a Friend be - side you, Keep a heart of sun-shine all the
as his own en - roll you, Keep a heart of sun-shine all the
start to - day for glo - ry, Keep a heart of sun-shine all the

CHORUS.

way.   Keep a heart of sun - shine all the way,
all the way.

Keep a heart of glad-ness ev - 'ry day; Let the Lord be near you,

Keep a Heart of Sunshine.

He'll sus-tain and cheer you, Keep a heart of sun-shine all the way.

5. The Name of Jesus.

W. C. Martin.   E. S. Lorenz.

1. The name of Je - sus is so sweet, I love its mu - sic to re-peat; It
2. I love the name of him whose heart Knows all my griefs and bears a part; Who
3. That name I fond - ly love to hear, It nev-er fails my heart to cheer, Its
4. No word of man can ev - er tell How sweet the name I love so well; Oh,

makes my joys full and com-plete, The precious name of Je - sus.
The precious name
bids all anx-ious fears de - part, I love the name of Je - sus.
I love the name
mu - sic dries the fall - ing tear; Ex - alt the name of Je - sus.
Ex - alt the name
let its prais-es ev - er swell! Oh, praise the name of Je - sus.
Oh, praise the name

p CHORUS.   *mf*

"Je-sus," oh, how sweet the name!" "Je-sus," ev - ry day the same,

"J e-sus," let all saints pro-claim Its wor - thy praise for - ev - er.
Its wor-thy praise

6.

Safe in the Harbor.

Ina Duley Ogdon.

Ira B. Wilson.

1. I was lost in the darkness and sor - row of sin, The tem-pest, the
2. Tho' beset by temp-ta-tions and driv - en by foes, His grace all - suf-
3. Let the clouds gather round me, the storms o'er me sweep, He ev-er is

conflict, with - out and with-in; Now in Je - sus, my Sav-ior, the
fi - cient, has conquered my woes, Since on Je - sus, my Sav-ior, my
with me to bless and to keep, For in Je - sus, my Sav-ior, my

dan - ger is past, I am safe in the har - bor at last.
bur - dens are cast, I am safe in the har - bor at last.
an - chor holds fast, I am safe in the har - bor at last.

D. S.—*I am safe in the har - bor at last.*

CHORUS.

I am safe in the har - bor at last, (at last,) The night of my

sor - row is past, (is past,) No harm can be - tide, in Him I a - bide,

7. I Need His Care.

Jennie Wilson. Clinton D. Lowden.

TWO PARTS.

1. From day to day I need the ten - der care...... Of Him, who al - ways
2. More val-ued in my Father's lov- ing sight..... I know this life of
3. I need his care and I will ev - er - claim .... In faith the help each

notes the sparrow's fall; ... And, oh, how sweet it is for me to feel .....
mine must surely be, ... Than is the bird or flow'r so small and frail:
day and hour demands, ... What-e'er the span of life to me may bring, ...

CHORUS.

That He will hear me when to Him I call....
Then will he not in love remember me?.... I need my Father's care, I
I glad-ly leave it in my Father's hands..

need his tender care, For oft my wea-ry way grows rough and dim; But love di-

vine, I know, will nev-er, nev-er fail, And it is sweet to trust in him.

8. What a Friend is Jesus.

C. R. F.

Carolyn R. Freeman.

1. Oft when the clouds are gloom-y and gray, Oft when the
2. Je-sus will jour-ney close to my side, Dai-ly my
3. When I am sad, to him will I go, With him the

day is drear-y, 'Tis then I hear a voice gent-ly say:
foot-steps lead-ing; Safe in his love I'll ev-er a-bide,
way grows bright-er; While his dear voice is mur-mur-ing low,

CHORUS.

"Let not your heart grow wea-ry."
Glad-ly his sweet voice heed-ing. Hark! 'tis the Sav-ior
Bur-dens and cares are light-er.

call-ing to me, Bid-ding me come to Je-sus, Soft-ly he

whis-pers, faith-ful I'll be; Oh, what a Friend is Je-sus.

9.

Even Me.

Elizabeth Codner.

Herm. von Berge.

1. Lord, I hear of show'rs of bless-ing Thou art scatt'ring full and free,
2. Pass me not, O gra - cious Father, Sin - ful tho' my heart may be;
3. Pass me not, O ten - der Sav-ior, Let me love and cling to thee;
4. Pass me not, O might - y Spir - it! Thou canst make the blind to see;

Show'rs, the thirsty land re-fresh-ing, Let thy blessing fall on me. E-ven
Thou mightst leave me, but the rath-er Let thy mer-cy fall on me. E-ven
I am long-ing for thy favor; Whilst thou'rt calling, oh, call me. E-ven
Wit - nes - ser of Je - sus' mer - it, Speak the word of pow'r to me. E-ven

me, e - ven me, Let them fall on e - ven me!
me, e - ven me, Gracious Fa - ther, e - ven me!
me, e - ven me, Ten-der Sav - ior, e - ven me!
me, e - ven me, Might-y Spir - it, e - ven me!

E-ven me, e-ven me, Let them fall on e - ven, e - ven me!
E-ven me, e-ven me, Gracious Father, e - ven, e - ven me!
E-ven me, e-ven me, Ten der Savior, e - ven, e - ven me!
E-ven me, e-ven me, Might y Spir-it, e - ven, e - ven me!

Show'rs, the thirsty land re - fresh-ing—Let thy bless-ing fall on me.
Thou mightst leave me, but the rather Let thy mer - cy fall on me.
I am long-ing for thy fa - vor, Whilst thou'rt calling, oh, call me.
Wit - nes - ser of Je - sus' mer - it, Speak the word of pow'r to me.

10. Are You Ready?

J. W. Slaughenhaupt.

E. S. Lorenz.

1. Soon the even-ing shad-ows fall-ing Close the day of mor-tal life;
2. Soon the aw-ful trum-pet sounding Calls thee to the judgment throne;
3. Oh, how fa-tal 'tis to lin-ger! Art thou read-y, read-y now?
4. Price-less love and free sal-va-tion Free-ly still are of-fered thee;

Soon the hand of death ap-pall-ing Draws thee from its wear-y strife.
Now pre-pare, for love a-bounding Yet has left thee not a-lone.
Read-y, should death's i-cy fin-ger Lay its chill up-on thy brow?
Yield no long-er to temp-tation, But from sin and sor-row flee.

CHORUS.

Are you ready? (Are you ready?) Are you read-y? (Are you ready?) 'Tis the

Spir-it calling, why de-lay? (Are you ready?) Are you ready? (Are you ready?)

Are you ready? (Are you ready?) Do not lin-ger longer, come to-day!

11. Some Day.

James Rowe.

B. D. Ackley.

1. Glad ho-san - nas we shall sing In the pal - ace of the King;
2. We shall meet our loved ones there, And their joys in heav-en share;
3. Then for-ev - er we shall be With the Christ of Cal - va - ry;

How our hap-py souls will shine In the light of love di - vine!
Voic - es which we hear no more, We shall hear on that glad shore.
And our voic-es we shall raise In an end-less song of praise.

CHORUS.

Some sweet day, Some sweet day,
Yes, some sweet day, Yes, some sweet day,

When our cares a - way are cast, Face to face with

day at last!

Him for - ev - er Some sweet day,............ at last!
some sweet day,

day at last!

12. Can I Forget?

Geo. O. Webster.

Ira B. Wilson.

DUET.

1. Can I for-get the love that stooped to earth, To seek and save, by way of
2. Can I for-get the pleadings and the tears In which He sought my love thro'
3. Can I for-get the scourging and the loss, The gar-den trag-e-dy, the

low-ly birth? The love that walked in distant Gal-i-lee The paths of
pa-tient years? Can I for-get the sweet "forgiveness word" So oft by
cru-el cross, The love He bore for sinners—e-ven me— The love that

bit-terness and want for me? ...
this re-pentant sin-ner heard? ..
fal-tered not on Cal-va-ry?

CHORUS.

Can I forget the crown of thorns He wore? Can I for-get the heav-y cross He bore? And can I e'er for-get, it was for me, He climbed the heights of Cal-va-ry?

13. In the Garden.

C. A. M.

C. Austin Miles.

1. I come to the gar-den a - lone, While the dew is still on the
2. He speaks, and the sound of his voice Is so sweet, the birds hush their
3. I'd stay in the gar-den with him, Tho' the night around me be

ros - es; And the voice I hear, Fall-ing on my ear, The
sing - ing, And the mel - o - dy That he gave to me, With-
fall - ing, But he bids me go; Thro' the voice of woe, His

Son of God dis - clos - es.
in my heart is ring - ing.
voice to me is call - ing.

CHORUS.

And he walks with me, and he

talks with me, And he tells me I am his own, And the

joy we share as we tar - ry there, None oth-er has ev - er known.

14. A Loving Word from You.

Rev. Alfred Barratt. Herm. von Berge.

1. There are man-y souls that have gone a-stray, They have wandered far
2. Let your life be bright, whit-er than the snow, Fill the world with light
3. Oh, what joy 'twill be, when this life is o'er, And you meet with those

from the nar-row way; You can win them back on this ver-y day
ev-'ry-where you go; Man-y ach-ing hearts with new life will glow,
who have gone be-fore, Who have found the way to the gold-en shore

CHORUS.

By a lov-ing word from you. By just a lov-ing
Just a word, a lov-ing

word from you, By just a lov-ing word from you; What a
word from you, just a word, a lov-ing word from you;

cheer-ing ray will il-lume life's way By a lov-ing word from you.

15. The Joy of the Lord.

Mattie B. Shannon.　　　　　　　　　　　　　　E. S. Lorenz.

1. Tho' hard be the task that the day's work may bring, There's strength always giv-
2. When tried by mis-fortune and sor-rows I see, There's joy in the love
3. I need not be wea-ry when he is my rest, Tho' cares may be fret-

en, it comes from my King, As on-ward I jour-ney I grate-ful-ly sing,
of my Sav-ior to me; He ev-er has promised my stronghold to be,
ting, by sins I am pressed; The love of my Sav-ior has man-y times blessed;

CHORUS.

The joy of the Lord is my strength. The joy of the Lord is my
strength! ..... The joy of the Lord is my strength! ...... How
is my strength!　　　　　　　　　　　　　　is my strength!

wondrous his love and the strength from above, The joy of the Lord is my strength!

16. The Church by the Side of the Road.

W. C. Poole.

B. D. Ackley.

1. Thro' the mist of years I can seem to see The church of my childhood days;
2. And the old, old songs that we used to sing, I'm sing-ing them o'er and o'er;
3. At the place of pray'r, in that lit-tle church, I knelt at my mother's side;
4. There's a hallowed spot 'neath the old pine tree, Where mother was laid to rest;

And its mem-'ries sweet, so with joy re-plete, Shall live in my heart al-ways.
They give strength and cheer when the clouds draw near, And lead to the oth-er shore.
There the Lord I found, it is ho-ly ground, The One who for sin-ners died.
What a joy 'twill be her dear face to see, With him that I love the best.

CHORUS. (*First four measures old melody.*)

Then on mem-o-ry's page I can see a-gain, The

rit.   *a tempo.*

church by the side of the road; (of the road;) And wher-

ev-er I roam, it is guiding me home, The church by the side of the road.

17.
Come Home.

May M. Brewster.   Ira B. Wilson.

1. I wandered a-way on the mountain of sin, A-far from my
2. Tho' help-less and wea-ry I heed-ed the call, I trust ed his
3. The Sav-ior is knocking with nail-pierc-ed hands, In mer-cy still

Fa-ther's home, But 'midst all the gloom there came un-to me
bound-less grace, Found com-fort and rest, my dark-ness dis-pelled
seeks the lost; The par-don and peace he of-fers to all,

Je-sus' voice say-ing ten-der-ly, "Come!"........   Come, home!
By the light of his won-der-ful face............
He has purchased at in-fin-ite cost............   Come!

Come home! The Sav-ior is call-ing to-day!.......
Come! ..   is call-ing to-day! His

love is so true, his heart yearns for you, Oh, come take the homeward way.

18. A Little Talk With Jesus.

J. P. Moorman.

DUET.

1. A lit - tle talk with Je - sus, How it smoothes the rug-ged road;
2. I'll tell him I am wea - ry, That I fain would be at rest,
3. I'll wait a lit - tle long - er, Till his own ap-point - ed time,

How it seems to help me onward, When I faint be-neath my load;
That I'm dai-ly, hour-ly longing For a home a - mong the blest;
And will glo - ry in the promise Of a pros - pect so sub - lime;

When my heart is crush'd with sor-row, And mine eyes with tears are dim,
For as yet the more I know him, And his mer - cy I ex-plore,
And when in my Father's dwelling, Where the ma - ny mansions be,

There is naught can yield me comfort, Like a lit - tle talk with him.
On - ly sets my heart to long-ing For a lit - tle talk the more.
I shall sweet-ly talk with Je - sus, And he will talk with me.

CHORUS. *Quartet.*

A lit - tle talk with Je - sus, How it smoothes the rugged road!

A Little Talk With Jesus.

There is naught can yield me com-fort Like a lit-tle talk with God.

19.   Jesus, Savior, Pilot Me.

Edward Hopper.   J. E. Gould. **Arr.**

1. Je-sus, Sav-ior, pi - lot me   O - ver life's tem-pes-tuous sea;
2. As a moth-er stills her child, Thou canst hush the o - cean wild;
3. When at last I reach the shore, And the fear - ful break-ers roar

Unknown waves before me roll,   Hiding rock and treach'rous shoal;
Boist'rous waves o-bey thy will, When thou say'st to them, "Be still!"
'Twixt me and the peace-ful rest, Then, while leaning on thy breast,

Chart and com pass come from thee, Je - sus, Sav - ior, pi - lot me.
Wond'rous Sov'reign of the sea, Je - sus, Sav - ior, pi - lot me.
May I hear thee say to me, "Fear not, I   will pi - lot thee."

20.

Sunrise Within.

Pearl Williams.

W. A. Post.

1. Have you the sun-rise of Je-sus with-in, Cast-ing out fear,
2. Have you the sun-rise of vic-to-ry now, O - ver the sin
3. Have you the sun-rise of hope and of peace, Ev - er so new,

bring-ing him near? Oh, how 'twill help in life's bat-tle to win!
lurk - ing with - in? Je - sus will cleanse if be - fore him you bow:
free - ly for you? Then shall your joy in the Lord nev - er cease;

CHORUS.

Have you the sun-rise with - in? Have you this sun-rise of
Have you the sun-rise with - in? Have you this

Je - sus with - in, Driv-ing a - way ev -'ry-thing that is sin?
sun - rise with - in, Driv - - ing a - way all of sin?

Oh, it will help you the vict'ry to win, O - ver and o - ver a - gain.

21. I Love Him.

Francis M. Morton.

Herm. von Berge.

1. I love my bless-ed Sav-ior When the days are bright and clear;
2. I know he will go with me, What-so-ev-er may be-tide;
3. Since love thro' all up-holds me, I shall sing a-long the way;

But just as much I love him, When the skies are dark and drear,
So why should I be fear-ful, With the Sav-ior for my Guide,
I love my bless-ed Sav-ior, And I trust him ev-'ry day,

Chorus.

When the skies are dark and drear.
With the Sav-ior for my Guide? All the way I love him, Ev-'ry
And I trust him ev-'ry day.

day I love Him; Just because I ful-ly trust him, I'm hap-py all the

way; Just be-cause I ful-ly trust him, I'm hap-py all the way.

22. Go Ye.

Mattie B. Shannon.   Norman Lighthill.

1. Are you will-ing to serve where-so-ev-er He will? For out o'er the
2. All the voi-ces of earth can-not si-lence this call, For down thro' the
3. Oh, the need is so great and the lab'rers so few, And somewhere is

high-ways the call ring-eth still! The Mas-ter is wait-ing, his
a - ges the clear ech-oes fall, The word of the Mas-ter is
wait-ing a task set for you; This day, in his serv-ice, his

CHORUS.

word now ful-fill: "Go ye! Go ye! Go ye!"
sound-ing to all: "Go ye! Go ye! Go ye!" In-to the world where his
bid-ding to do, "Go ye! Go ye! Go ye!"

creat-ures are found, Forth in his might that his word may a-bound, Till

Christ's name shall cir-cle the whole earth a-round; "Go ye! Go ye! Go ye!"

23. Speak a Word for Jesus.

J. T. Latta.

Ira B. Wilson.

1. Speak a word for Je - sus, To the un-saved near; Speak a word, 'twill
2. Speak a word for Je - sus, Speak un-to the lost; Tell them for their
3. Speak a word for Je - sus, Spread the message wide That for ev - 'ry

help them; Speak a word of cheer. Tell them of his mer-cy, Tell them of his
e - vil He has paid the cost; Tell them he is wait-ing Them to bless to-
sin - ner Je-sus Christ has died; Tell them that his friendship Faithful is and

love; Tell them of sal - va - tion, And the home a - bove.
day; Ask them to ac - cept him; He's the on - ly way.
true; Speak a word for Je - sus; Some one spoke to you.

CHORUS.

Speak .... a word...... Speak...... a word. .
Speak a word, speak a word, Speak a word for Je - sus!

rit.

With a song of cour-age strong, Go tell the world of him.

24. Forgiven.

Mattie B. Shannon.　　　　　　　　　　　　E. S. Lorenz.

1. There's a word of wondrous beau-ty, 'Tis the sweet-est ev-er heard;
2. To my Lord in deep con-tri-tion, Tho' like scar-let was my sin,
3. Ye who know not Christ's re-demp-tion, Nor the sweet-ness of his peace,

It has filled my life with glad-ness, All my soul with joy has stirred;
Did I come for ut-ter cleans-ing, Glad his ho-li-ness to win;
Have not felt the joy of par-don, Have not won from sin re-lease,

For it means that Christ, my Sav-ior, From my sin has set me free;
How in-spir-ing was his par-don, And his peace how wondrous sweet!
'Tis for you, the bless-ed mes-sage, That with joy to you we bear;

Yes, it means at home in heav en fair, I'll dwell e-ter-nal-ly.
Now a-round his throne in glo-ry-land, The ransomed I will meet.
You may join the white-robed throng in song A-round his throne so fair.

CHORUS.

For-giv-en! For-giv-en! 'Tis a word with wondrous pow'r! For-

Forgiven.

giv - en! For - giv - en! To live with Christ each hour! O thou

love of God so won-drous! O thou grace so full and free! For-

giv - en! For - giv - en! I'll serve E - ter - nal - ly.

e - ter - nal - ly,

25. Now the Day is Over.

S. Baring-Gould.   Joseph Barnby.

1. Now the day is o - ver; Night is draw - ing nigh;
2. Thro' the long night-watch - es, May Thine an - gels spread
3. When the morn - ing wak - ens, Then may I a - rise,

Shad - ows of the even - ing Steal a - cross the sky.
Their white wings a - bove me, Watch - ing 'round my bed.
Pure, and fresh, and sin - less, In Thy ho - ly eyes.

even - ing Steal a - cross the sky.

26. If Only Thy Will be Done.

May Justus.   Herm. von Berge.

1. Let me, Lord, my way for-get, If on-ly thy will be done;
2. Bid me go, or bid me stay, If on-ly thy will be done;
3. Take my years of ser-vice free, If on-ly thy will be done;

be done!..
Let me yield without re gret, If on-ly thy will, thy will be done!
Pleasant path, or rug-ged way, If on-ly thy will, thy will be done!
Oh, it is e-nough for me, If on-ly thy will, thy will be done!

rit.
What am I that I should choose? What is mine to take or use?
Be it crown or be it cross, Be it gain or bit-ter loss:
Peace I find up-on thy breast, Calm-ly all on thee I rest;

a tempo.
All my-self I glad-ly lose, If on-ly thy will be done.
All I have I count but dross, If on-ly thy will be done.
E-ven death with thee is best, If on-ly thy will be done.

CHORUS.
If on - ly thy will be done; If on - ly thy will be done!
If on-ly thy will be done, If on-ly thy will be done!

If Only Thy Will be Done.

rit.

In joy, in care, be this my pray'r: If on-ly thy will be done!.....
thy will be done!

a tempo.

For lo !..... I am not my own, Dear Lord,.... I am thine a-lone;
For lo! I am not my own, Dear Lord, I am thine a-lone;

In all my ways, thro' all my days, Thy will be.... done!
Let on-ly thy will be done!

27. ## Jesus Calls Us.

Mrs. C. F. Alexander.   W. H. Jude.

1. Je-sus calls us; o'er the tu-mult Of our life's wild, restless sea;
2. Je-sus calls us from the wor - ship Of the vain world's golden store;
3. Je-sus calls us by his mer - cies; Sav- ior, may we hear thy call!

Day by day his sweet voice soundeth, Saying, "Christian, fol-low me!"
From each i - dol that would keep us, Saying, "Christian, love me more!"
Give our hearts to thy o - bedience, Serve and love thee best of all!

29

28. Choose My Path.

May M. Brewster.

Ira B. Wilson.

1. Thou who dost hear the cry of e'en the hum-blest,
2. Teach me Thy will, that ev-er I may fol-low
3. What-e'er be-tide, with Thy strong arm to shel-ter,

To Thee I call on bend-ed knee; Thou who dost know my
Where Thou dost lead, in storm or shine, Nev-er a-lone, but
Help me to say, Thy will be done! My soul at last tri-

heart's de-sire and long-ing, Oh, wilt Thou choose my path for me?
in Thy pres-ence dwell-ing; Then I shall know Thy peace di-vine.
umph-ant shall be sing-ing, Thro' Thee the vic-t'ry shall be won.

CHORUS.

On Thee I call, who know-est all, My bur-dens and my fears;
Thy way

Thy way is best, in Thee I'll rest A-down the pass-ing years.
is best, in

29.

God is Love.

E. S. Lorenz.

1. Come, come, come! Come, let us al u-nite to sing, God is love!
2. Gome, come, come! Oh, tell to earth's re-mot-est bounds, God is love!
3. Come, come, come! How hap-py is our por-tion here, God is love!

Let heav'n and earth their praises bring, God is love! Let ev-ry soul from
In Christ we have redemption found, God is love! His blood has washed our
His prom-is-es our spir-its cheer, God is love! He is our sun and

sin a-wake, Each in his heart sweet mu-sic make, And sing with us for
sins a-way, His spir-it turned our night to day; And now we can re-
shield by day, Our help, our hope, our strength and stay; He will be with us

REFRAIN.

Je-sus' sake, For God is love. God is love!
joice to say That God is love.
all the way; Our God is love. God is love! God is

God is love! Come, let us all u-nite to sing That God is love!
love! .....

30. Closer to Thee.

Rev. W. C. Poole.

B. D. Ackley.

1. Clos - er and clos - er, dear Sav - ior, Near - er and near - er to thee; Where e - vil can - not o'er - take me, There would my soul ev - er be.
2. Clos - er and clos - er, oh, draw me, Hold me, yes, hold thou me near; On - ly thy love shall con - trol me, Noth - ing of ill shall I fear.
3. When in my fal - ter - ing weak - ness, Ev - er I wan - der a - lone; Fold me, dear Mas - ter, oh, fold me, And keep me whol - ly thine own.
4. When the dark shadows of even - ing Gath - er a - round me, I pray, Dear Sav - ior, hold me still clos - er, While ends life's wea - ri - some day.

CHORUS.

Clos - er and clos - er, till I'm so near, Thy faint - est whis - per to me, I can hear; Clos - er and clos - er, till I can say, "Noth - ing of self, Lord, but all of thee."

31. In My Heart the Joy-Bells.

May Justus.

Ira B. Wilson.

1. The peace of God is in my soul to-day; In sweetest faith I
2. No fear have I of foes that may as-sail; No dread is mine that
3. Unknown the way that goes in-to the west, But on I go—the

la-bor as I pray; The bless-ed Mas-ter walks a-long the way, And
e-vil shall prevail; The Master's might-y pow'r can nev-er fail, And
Master's will is best, And they who fol-low him are hap-pi-est; For-

f CHORUS.

in my heart the bells of joy are ring-ing.
in my heart the bells of joy are ring-ing. Joy-bells, joy-bells,
ev-er will my bells of joy be ring-ing.

In my hap-py heart the mu-sic swells; (O love divine;) O love di-vine,

O rapture that is mine, For in my heart the bells of joy are ring-ing.

32.   Day is Dying in the West.

Mary A. Lathbury.   W. F. Sherwin.

1. Day is dy-ing in the west; Heav'n is touch-ing
2. Lord of life, be-neath the dome Of the u-ni-

earth with rest: Wait and wor-ship while the night Sets her even-ing
verse, thy home, Gath-er us who seek thy face To the fold of

pp REFRAIN. *p*

lamps a-light Thro' all the sky. Ho-ly, ho-ly,
thy em-brace, For thou art nigh.

m *f*

ho-ly, Lord God of Hosts! Heav'n and earth are full of thee!

Heav'n and earth are prais-ing thee, O Lord most high.

33. I Belong to Jesus.

H. v. B.   Herm. von Berge.

1. Oh, the blessed consciousness in my soul: By His pow'r I'm saved, and by
2. Day by day I walk with him at my side; He's my lov-ing Savior, my
3. In   unfail-ing love does he with me bear, When so oft temptations my
4. Some day I shall stand from all blemish free, With the saints in glo-ry, my

grace made whole; And the heav'nly mansions are now my goal, For I be-
Friend and Guide; He will nev-er fail me, what-e'er be-tide, For I be-
soul   en-snare; And he heals my bruises with ten-der care, For I be-
Lord   to see; But he knows me now and he cares for me, For I be-

Chorus

long to Je - sus. I am his and, oh, I know that he is mine; Naught can
long to Je - sus.
long to Je - sus.
long to Je - sus.   I be-long, I be-long   to   Je-sus;

ev - er change his boundless love di - vine. I can trust him to the
I be - long, I be-long   to   Je-sus.

end, He my ev - er-last-ing Friend, And I be-long to Je - sus.

34.

Wonderful Word.

Geo. O. Webster.

Ira B. Wilson.

Melody of verse in First Alto.

1. Wonder-ful Word of our Fa-ther in heav'n, Guide-Book unfail-ing—in
2. Wonder-ful Word with its mes-sage of joy, Hope for the sin-ful that
3. Wonder-ful Word to the lone-ly in tears, Prom-ise of strength 'mid our

love it is giv'n; Lamp for our feet 'mid earth's darkness and strife—
naught can de-stroy; Buck-ler and shield when temp-ta-tions are rife—
tri-als and fears, Light for earth's darkness and help in its strife—

CHORUS

Won-der-ful Book of life. Won - der-ful sto-ry,
Won-der-ful Book of life.
Won-der-ful Book of life. Thine is a won-der-ful sto-ry,

Point - ing to glo-ry, The light from thy pag-es Il-
Point-ing the path-way to glo-ry,

lu-mines the a-ges, O won-der-ful Book of Life.

35. The Light of Lights is Jesus.

W. C. Poole.　　　　　　　　　　　　　　E. S. Lorenz.

1. There is a light that nev-er fails, But ev-er shines a-mid the night,
2. There is a light that, thro' the dark, Sends out its beams to shine a - far
3. There is a light that will shine on Thro' all the countless years of time;
4. There is a light, and it is mine, To guide when other lights are dim;

And o - ver ev - 'ry cloud prevails With rainbows full of glo-ry bright.
And guide the lost and sinking bark In - to the port across the bar.
When other lights have failed and gone The Son of God will shine sub-lime.
And thro' the night my light di-vine Is Je-sus, and I walk with him.

CHORUS.

Your light and mine! Your light and mine!'Twill brightly shine o'er land and sea,

Your light and mine! Now, thro' all e - ter-ni-ty, Now, thro' all e-

ter - ni-ty,　　　　　　The light of lights, The light of lights is Je - sus!
The light of lights,

36. Where He Leads.

May M. Brewster.

Roy E. Nolte.

1. Not al - ways through...... rich pastures green,...... My
2. Not al - ways by........... the wa - ters still,......... Some-
3. So whether on.......... the hill-tops fair,.. .... Or

way ... is oft - times drear - y; Yet Je - sus leads,.......
times .. the waves sweep o'er me; But midst it all, ...
through dark val - leys go - ing, No mat - ter where,........

my soul he feeds,........ And com - forts me when wea - ry.
I hear his call,........ For Je - sus goes be - fore me.
still he is there,........ His gra - cious kind - ness show - ing.

REFRAIN.

Days of joy........ or days of sor - row,
Days of joy, or days of sor - row, days of sor - row,

Nev - er anx - - ious fears I'll bor - row;
Nev - er anx - ious fears I'll bor - row, will I bor - row,

Where He Leads.

There will come........ a glad to-mor-row,
There will come a glad to-mor-row, glad to-mor-row,

For I fol-low where he leads, I will fol-low where he leads.

37. Hear My Prayer.

Anon.   George S. Schuler.

1. Not more of light, I ask, O God, But eyes to see what is;.....
2. Not more of joy, but pow'r to feel Its kindling pres-ence near;
3. Give me all fears to dom-i-nate, All ho-ly joys to know;
4. Yet more of thee, I ask, O God, To be what I should be;.....

Not sweeter songs, but pow'r to hear The pres-ent mel-o-dies......
To give to oth-ers all I have Of cour-age and of cheer......
To be the friend I wish to be, To speak the truth I know......
Help me in all I do, to live A ho-ly life for thee. ...

REFRAIN.   *After last verse only.*

Hear my pray'r, hear my pray'r! Heav'nly Father, hear my pray'r. Hear my pray'r.
Hear, oh, hear my pray'r!

Copyright, 1925, by Lorenz Publishing Co., in "The Choir Herald" for September, 1925.
International copyright.
Arrangement Copyright, 1925, by Lorenz Publishing Co., in "Women's New Gospel Quartets."
International copyright.

38. Come Closer to Me.

H. v. B.

Herm. v. Berge.

1. Come closer, my child! Oh, why art thou roaming So oft-en, a-
2. Come closer, my child! Why art thou fore-go-ing The joy and the
3. Come closer, my child! Tho' high in the heav-ens An un-num-bered

las, in thine own erring way? Come closer, my child, and cease from thy
peace that in ful-ness are thine, If thou wilt but come, thy her-it-age
host be surrounding the throne, Tho' all thro' the world the lov-ing de-

wan-d'ring, There's nothing but loss in thy go-ing a-stray.
claim-ing, And take for thine own all the bless-ings di-vine!
vo-tion Of serv-ants of mine and my chil-dren I own;

Oh, give not thine ear to the world's tempt-ing plea:
If life o-ver-flow-ing thou long-est to see,
My heart yet hath need, my be-lov-ed, of thee:

Slow and tenderly.

Come closer, my child, to me; Come clos-er, my child, to me.

39. May God Depend on You?

W. C. Martin.

Ira B. Wilson.

1. In the war-fare that is rag-ing For the truth and for the right,
2. See, they come on sa-ble pin-ions, Come they in Sa-tan-ic might,
3. From his throne the Fa-ther sees us; An-gels help us to pre-vail;

When the con-flict fierce is rag-ing With the pow-ers of the night,
Pow-ers come and dark do-min-ions From the re-gions of the night.
And our lead-er true is Je-sus, And we shall not, can-not fail.

God needs peo-ple brave and true: May he then de-pend on you?
God re-quires the brave and true, May he there de-pend on you?
Tri-umph crowns the brave and true, May the Lord de-pend on you?
peo - ple brave and true,

CHORUS.

May the Lord.. de-pend on you?.. Loy-al-ty... is but his due;..
May the Lord de-pend on you? Loy-al-ty is but his due;

Say, O spir-it brave and true, That he may de-pend on you.
spir - it brave and true,

40. His Face is Shining o'er Me.

Rene Bronner.

Ira B. Wilson.

1. At ev-en-tide, when day is done, And all its cares are laid at rest, The
2. When sorrow falls upon my heart, And lifeless seems the hope I crave, I
3. When at the parting of the ways I come to cross the rolling sea, His

face of Je-sus seems to come, And I with joy am doub-ly blessed.
see a-gain his smil-ing face, With pow'r to comfort and to save.
face will light me to the shore, For-ev-er-more with him to be.

CHORUS.

His face is shin-ing o'er me ev-'ry day, His grace suf-fi-

cient for me all the way; Un-to the end he is my

rit.

faith-ful Guide, And in his love I ev-er shall a-bide.

41.

Until He Finds.

May M. Brewster.   E. S. Lorenz.

1. O ten-der, loving Shepherd, e'er seeking those who roam, O'er rug-ged mountains climb-ing to bring the wand'rers home. How long wouldst thou be will-ing this lone-ly way to keep, Amidst the storm and darkness, to find a straying sheep?

2. 'Twas then the Shepherd answered, in gentle tones and sweet, As still in love he fol-lowed with wea-ry, bleeding feet: "I count not days and moments, as thou the years dost bind, The length of all my seek-ing is just un-til I find."

3. 'Far out on burning desert, or where the fierce winds blow, Wher-e'er my lost ones per-ish, o'er an-y path I'll go; No night too dark and drear-y, no wa-ters e'er too deep, I'll ne'er return from searching, un-til I find my sheep"

REFRAIN.

O'er mount-ains wild and steep, O'er mount-ains wild and steep, The Shep-herd true is seek-ing To find a stray-ing sheep."

In gen - tle tones and kind, In gen - tle tones and kind, The Shep-herd's voice is say-ing, "I seek un - til I find."

Tho' wave and flood are deep, Tho' wave and flood are deep, The Shep-herd's love is bound-less, Re-joice! he finds his sheep.

42. 'Tis the Same Old Flag.

C. R. F.

Carolyn R. Freeman.

1. Once in the by - gone ag - es, Just at our na-tion's morn,
2. Al - ways in days of dan - ger, Oft 'neath a dark-ened sky,
3. As in the ear - ly morn-ing, Thus may she ev - er be,

There, 'mid the gray of dawn-ing, A - mer - i - ca's flag was born.
Thro' all the din of bat - tle, So proud-ly she waves on high.
Em - blem of land vic - to - rious, The pride of the brave and free.

CHORUS. *Two-Parts.*

The same old flag, old glory, Floats on the morn-ing air,
The flag of no-ble father's, Flag of their sons so true,

'Tis the same old flag, old glory, That floats on the morning air,
'Tis the flag of no-ble fathers, The flag of their sons so true,

1

Colors bright, field of white, Speak of treasures fair.

And the colors bright, on a field of white, Speak of treasures wondrous fair.

'Tis the Same Old Flag.

And the stars and stripes for-ev-er, Are our own red, white and blue.

43. ## Stand Up for Jesus.

George Duffield.

J. J. Webb.

1. Stand up! stand up for Je-sus! Ye sol-diers of the cross;
2. Stand up! stand up for Je-sus! Stand in his strength a-lone;
3. Stand up! stand up for Je-sus! The strife will not be long;

FINE.

Lift high his roy-al ban-ner, It must not suf-fer loss:
The arm of flesh will fail you— Ye dare not trust your own.
This day the noise of bat-tle, The next the vic-tor's song:

D. S.-Till ev-'ry foe is van-quished, And Christ is Lord in-deed.
D. S.-Where du-ty calls, or dan-ger, Be nev-er want-ing there.
D. S.-He, with the King of glo-ry, Shall reign e-ter-nal-ly.

D. S.

From vic-t'ry un-to vic-t'ry His ar-my shall he lead,
Put on the gos-pel ar-mor, And, watching un-to pray'r,
To him that o-ver-com-eth, A crown of life shall be;

44.

Tell It All to Him.

Rene Bronner.   Ira B. Wilson.

1. There are days when we are lone-ly, There are days when we are sad, When the
2. There are days when we are restless, There are days when we are weak, When we
3. There are days when we are hap-py, There are days when we are glad, When the

tasks that heap up - on us Bring no hours to make us glad. Then to Him who bore the
turn from all that's pre-cious, And the things of sin we seek. Then to Him of great for-
joys of life and liv - ing Leave no room to make us sad. Then it is our hearts should

sor - rows Of the world, we humbly turn, Knowing He a lone will hear us,
give - ness, We our hearts may o-pen wide, Filled with sinful tho'ts and fan-cies,
praise Him, Fill-ing all the world with cheer, Tell-ing those who dwell in sor - row,

CHORUS.

Bring the peace for which we yearn.
And may all to Him con - fide.   Tell it all to Him, All your hearts e'er hold,
He a - lone their griefs will hear.

poco rit.   *a tempo.*

In His lov - ing pres - ence Ev - 'ry-thing un-fold; Seek His guid-ance

Tell It All to Him.

f rit.

All a-long the way; Faith-ful you will find Him, Tell Him all to - day.

45.

We Will Follow Jesus.

Anon.

Herm. von Berge.

1. "Fol - low Me," the Mas - ter said; We will fol - low Je - sus;
2. Should the world and sin op - pose, We will fol - low Je - sus;
3. Tho' the way may dark ap - pear, We will fol - low Je - sus;

By his word and Spir - it led, We will fol - low Je - sus.
He is great - er than our foes; We will fol - low Je - sus.
He will make our path - way clear; We will fol - low Je - sus.

Still for us he lives to plead, At the throne to in - ter - cede,
On his prom - ise we de - pend; He will suc - cor and de - fend,
In our dai - ly round of care, As we plead with God in prayer,

Of - fers help in time of need: We will fol - low Je - sus.
Help and keep us to the end: We will fol - low Je - sus.
With the cross which we must bear, We will fol - low Je - sus.

46. There is Joy in His Presence.

Clarence E. Flynn.

E. S. Lorenz.

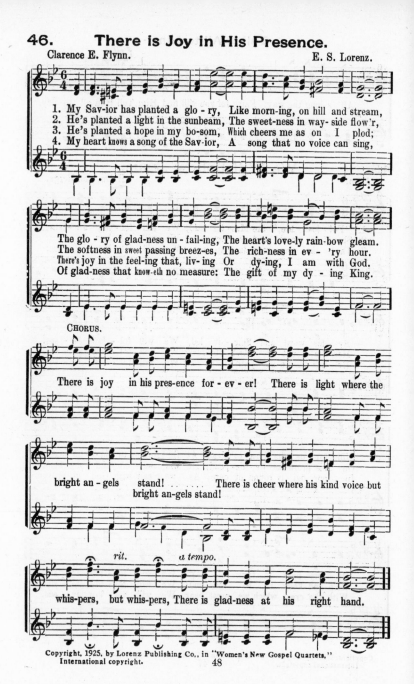

1. My Sav-ior has planted a glo-ry, Like morn-ing, on hill and stream,
2. He's planted a light in the sunbeam, The sweet-ness in way-side flow'r,
3. He's planted a hope in my bos-om, Which cheers me as on I plod;
4. My heart knows a song of the Sav-ior, A song that no voice can sing,

The glo-ry of glad-ness un-fail-ing, The heart's love-ly rain-bow gleam.
The softness in sweet passing breez-es, The rich-ness in ev-'ry hour.
There's joy in the feel-ing that, liv-ing Or dy-ing, I am with God.
Of glad-ness that know-eth no measure: The gift of my dy-ing King.

CHORUS.

There is joy in his pres-ence for-ev-er! There is light where the

bright an-gels stand! ...... There is cheer where his kind voice but
bright an-gels stand!

rit. *a tempo.*

whis-pers, but whis-pers, There is glad-ness at his right hand.

47.

Mine.

W. C. Poole.

Fred. B. Holton.

1. I have light in the darkness, I have peace di - vine, I have calm in the
2. I've a won-der-ful treasure, I have joy un - told, I have mansions in
3. I have Je-sus for-ev - er, Savior, Friend divine, And he fail-eth me

tem-pest, Je - sus now is mine.
glo - ry, Nev-er to grow old.   Mine when the bil-lows are rag - ing,
nev - er, He is ev - er mine.

CHORUS.

Mine in the dark-ness of night, Mine when the foe is en-gag - ing,

poco rit.

Mine in the morning bright; Mine when the tempter is call - ing, I have

One di - vine, Ev - er his blessings are fall-ing, He is mine, mine, mine!

48. The City of God.

J. B. Atchison. Chorus by I. B. W.

Ira B. Wilson.

Two-Parts.

1. I have read.... of a beau - ti - ful cit - y,
2. I have read.... of bright man - sions in heav - en,
3. I have read ... of white robes for the right - eous,

rit.

Far a - way.... in the king - dom of God;....
Which the Sav - ior has gone to pre - pare;....
Of bright crowns which the glo - ri - fied wear;....

a tempo.

I have read ... how its walls.... are of jas - per,
And the saints.. who on earth.... have been faith - ful,
And our Fa - ther shall bid ..... us "Come en - ter,

rit.

How its streets are all gol - den and broad.
Rest for - ev - er with Christ o - ver there."
And my glo - ry e - ter - nal - ly share."

The City of God.

CHORUS. *Four-Parts.* *A tempo.*

Beauti-ful, beauti-ful cit-y of God, Of all the faithful the promised abode;

Glories untold in that cit-y of gold, Beauti-ful cit-y of God.

49. My Task.

Maude Louise Ray and S. H. Pickup.   E. L. Ashford.

1. To love some one more dearly ev-'ry day,... To help a wand'ring
2. To fol - low truth as blind men long for light, To do my best from
3. And then my Sav - ior by and by to meet, When faith hath made her

child to find his way,... To ponder o'er a no-ble tho't and pray,
dawn of day till night, To keep my heart fit for his ho-ly sight,
task on earth com - plete, And lay my homage at the Master's feet,

And smile when evening falls, And smile when evening falls, This is my task.
And answer when he calls, And answer when he calls, This is my task.
Within the jas-per walls, Within the jas-per walls, This crown's my task.

50. We are Saved to Serve.

May Justus.

E. S. Lorenz.

1. It is not e-nough to be saved from sin, With no foes with-out and no fears with-in; There's a greater joy that we all may win:
2. It is not e-nough to have found a light, And to let it shine on your path-way bright; Hold it up for one who is yet in night:
3. It is not e-nough to be safe at home While so man-y wan-der a-far and roam; It is not e-nough till you bid them, "Come,"

CHORUS.

We are saved to serve to-day! We are saved to serve! We are saved to serve! We are saved to serve to - day! 'Tis a

saved to serve to - day!

tried, true test, They who love Him best, Labor glad-ly all the way.

51.

All is Well.

Mary Peters.

Herm. von Berge.

All will be well;

1. Thro' the love of Christ, our Sav-ior, All is well;
2. Tho' we pass thro' trib-u-la-tion, All is well;
3. We shall see a bright to-mor-row, All is well;

Free and change-less is his fa-vor, And all is well.
Ours is such a full sal-va-tion, And all is well.
Faith can sing thro' days of sor-row, For all is well.

Precious is the blood that healed us, Per-fect is the grace that
Hap-py still in him con-fi-ding, Fruit-ful if in Christ a-
On our Father's love re-ly-ing, Je-sus ev-'ry need sup-

sealed us, Strong the hand stretched out to shield us, And all is
bid-ing, Ho-ly thro' the Spir-it's guid-ing, And all is
ply-ing, Be it liv-ing, be it dy-ing, All, all is

Slow and emphatic.

well; Strong the hand stretched out to shield us: All is well!
well; Ho-ly thro' the Spir-it's guid-ing: All is well!
well: Be it liv-ing, be it dy-ing: All is well!

52. Sweet Hour of Devotion.

Fanny J. Crosby. Ira B. Wilson.

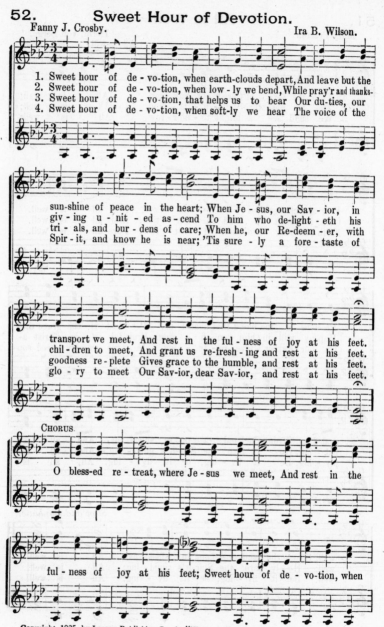

1. Sweet hour of de-vo-tion, when earth-clouds depart, And leave but the
2. Sweet hour of de-vo-tion, when low-ly we bend, While pray'r and thanks-
3. Sweet hour of de-vo-tion, that helps us to bear Our du-ties, our
4. Sweet hour of de-vo-tion, when soft-ly we hear The voice of the

sun-shine of peace in the heart; When Je-sus, our Sav-ior, in
giv-ing u-nit-ed as-cend To him who de-light-eth his
tri-als, and bur-dens of care; When he, our Re-deem-er, with
Spir-it, and know he is near; 'Tis sure-ly a fore-taste of

transport we meet, And rest in the ful-ness of joy at his feet.
chil-dren to meet, And grant us re-fresh-ing and rest at his feet.
goodness re-plete Gives grace to the humble, and rest at his feet.
glo-ry to meet Our Sav-ior, dear Sav-ior, and rest at his feet.

CHORUS.

O bless-ed re-treat, where Je-sus we meet, And rest in the

ful-ness of joy at his feet; Sweet hour of de-vo-tion, when

Sweet Hour of Devotion.

earth-clouds de - part, And leave but the sun-shine of peace in the heart.

53.

Evening Song.

Wm. H. Gardner.

B. D. Ackley.

1. As the eve - ning shadows fall, As the night-winds mournful call,
2. Man-y shattered hopes we've seen, Flown has man - y a gold-en dream,
3. Shadows dark and bit - ter tears Have we known thro' man - y years,

As we end our earth-ly days, Still we sing our song of praise.
Yet as backward now we gaze, Still we sing our song of praise.
Yet at close of life we raise, Still to thee our song of praise.

CHORUS.

Thou hast led us, bless-ed Sav - ior, Safe-ly o'er the drea - ry wold,

Soon we'll find sweet rest e - ter - nal In the Fa-ther's heav'nly fold.

54. My Redeemer.

L. M. G.   Lottie M. Gage.

1. There is glo - ry in the sun- set, There is beau - ty all a - round;
2. See the flow'rs' unfading splen- dor In that ho - ly cit - y fair,
3. Oh, the joy that there a-waits me When my heav'nly Friend I meet!

God has plant - ed here the sunbeams, Ev'rywhere can joy be found.
See the an - gels' shin-ing rai-ment, As in peace they're dwelling there.
Oh, the rap - ture and the glo - ry I shall know when Christ I greet!

What is this, compared with heav-en, With its shin - ing streets of gold?
They are there with Christ, the Savior, And with him I long to be,
Just to see him in the beau - ty Of his ten - der-ness and love!

What is this, compared with Je-sus, And his maj - es - ty un-told?
For I'm look-ing for the homeland, Where his bless-ed face I'll see.
Just to clasp the hand that led me Safe-ly to the home a-bove.

CHORUS.

Yes, he is my dear Re-deem - er, And the Sav - ior of my soul;

My Redeemer.

He will guide me, he will keep me, While the end - less ag - es roll.

55. In That Fair Land.

Rene Bronner.

Ira B. Wilson.

1. There is a hope that guides us on Be-yond the goal of wait-ing years,
2. There is a voice that whispers low In-to our hearts when danger's near,
3. There is a way for wand'ring feet, That leads to life be-yond the skies,

As   one by one we jour-ney on Where joy and love will dry our tears.
And tells us of a place be-yond, Where we shall rest with-out a fear.
Where all the good will find a home, Where love and friendship nev-er dies.

CHORUS.

Be-yond the vale, be-yond the years, Be-yond the cares, be-yond the tears,

We'll find a home be-yond the skies, In that fair land of Par - a - dise.

56.
He Promised Me.

H. v. B.

Herm. von Berge.

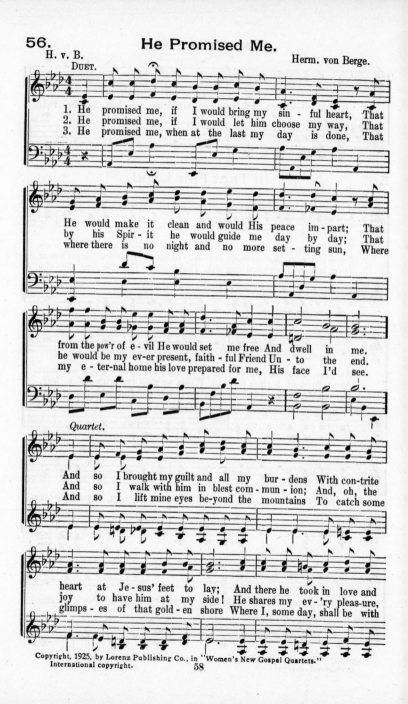

DUET.

1. He promised me, if I would bring my sin - ful heart, That
2. He promised me, if I would let him choose my way, That
3. He promised me, when at the last my day is done, That

He would make it clean and would His peace im - part; That
by his Spir - it he would guide me day by day; That
where there is no night and no more set - ting sun, Where

from the pow'r of e - vil He would set me free And dwell in me.
he would be my ev - er present, faith - ful Friend Un - to the end.
my e - ter - nal home his love prepared for me, His face I'd see.

Quartet.

And so I brought my guilt and all my bur - dens With con-trite
And so I walk with him in blest com - mun - ion; And, oh, the
And so I lift mine eyes be-yond the mountains To catch some

heart at Je - sus' feet to lay; And there he took in love and
joy to have him at my side! He shares my ev - 'ry pleas-ure,
glimps - es of that gold - en shore Where I, some day, shall be with

He Promised Me.

ten-der mer-cy My sins a-way, my sins a-way.
ev-'ry sor-row, My heav'n-ly Guide, my heav'n-ly Guide.
my Re-deem-er For-ev-er-more, for-ev-er-more.

57. Christ Meets My Every Need.

Lizzie DeArmond.   E. S. Lorenz.

1. Tho' tri - als oft like tempests sweep,   A Friend I have in-deed;
2. Tho' round my path the shadows fall,   My Lord will surely lead;
3. "Lo! I   am with you, do not fear,"   Within his Word I read;
1. Tho' tri-als oft   like tempests sweep, A Friend I have indeed;

There's One whose pow'r will safely keep;... Christ meets my ev'ry need.
His love   divine has planned it all,   Christ meets my ev-'ry need.
Tho' I   must face temptations here,   Christ meets my ev-'ry need.
There's One whose pow'r will   safely keep;

CHORUS.

Christ meets my need, whate'er it be! Christ meets my need, my help is he!

Christ meets my need along life's way,..... He meets my need from day to day.
                    toil-some way,

58.

Have Mercy On Me.

Fanny J. Crosby. (Posthumous.)

B. D. Ackley.

1. I come as I am, for I dare not de-lay, My life like a
shad-ow is fly-ing a-way; I come as I am with my
bur-den to Thee, And this my pe-ti-tion: have mer-cy on me.

2. I come as I am, for thy voice I have heard, A-gain, and a-
gain, in thy life-giv-ing Word; Thou call-est the wea-ry to
come un-to thee, O bless-ed Re-deem-er, have mer-cy on me.

3. I come as I am, and thy par-don im-plore, For hast thou not
promised my soul to re-store? I long from this bur-den of
sin to be free, O Sav-ior, dear Sav-ior, have mer-cy on me.

CHORUS.

Have mer-cy on me; have mer-cy on me; Dear
Sav-ior, have mer-cy on me; I thirst for the well of sal-

Have Mercy On Me.

va - tion so free, O Je - sus, have mer - cy on me.

59.   **Let Jesus Have His Way.**

Clarence E. Flynn.   John D. Creswell.

1. In ev - 'ry task your hands may do, Let Je - sus have his way;
2. In ev - 'ry love your heart may know, Let Je - sus have his way;
3. In ev - 'ry hope you cher - ish deep, Let Je - sus have his way;

In ev - 'ry road you trav - el, too, Let Je - sus have his way.
In ev - 'ry joy and ev - 'ry woe, Let Je - sus have his way.
In ev - 'ry pur - pose that you keep, Let Je - sus have his way.

He'll make the task a hap - py one, The jour - ney you will glad - ly run;
Your love the Lord will sanc - ti - fy, Your joy will grow, your sor - row die;
The hope he'll cleanse and rich - ly bless, The pur - pose bring to fruit - ful - ness;

All roads are gold - en with the sun, When Je - sus has his way.
There's naught but sun - shine in the sky, When Je - sus has his way.
And it was best, you will con - fess, For him to have his way.

Copyright, 1925, by Lorenz Publishing Co., in "The Volunteer Choir" for June, 1923.
International copyright.

60. Lord, Give Me Love.

May Justus.   Herm. von Berge.

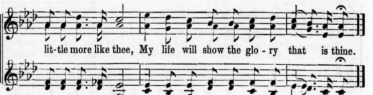

1. Lord, give me love, with which to serve to - day, And love to
2. So few the days, so man - y wand'ring feet; Lord, send me
3. When ends at last my toil at thy be hest, Be - fore I

see who needs me on the way; For I would be a fol-low-er of
forth, some brother soul to meet, That I may say, 'Come, see the Lord to-
en - ter thine e - ter-nal rest, Oh, may I see some oth-er safe with

CHORUS.

thee, And I would love, and I would love to-day.
day!" Make me a her-ald of thy mes-sage sweet. Lord, give me of the love
me, To share the heav'nly glo-ry of the blest.

that is divine! Lord, give me of thy love, and make it mine! Thus I shall be a

lit-tle more like thee, My life will show the glo - ry that is thine.

I Will Follow Anywhere.

Geo. O. Webster.　　　　　　　　　　　　　Ira B. Wilson.

1. In paths of light my Lord may lead me, Up rug-ged height,
2. In pain and loss up Calv'ry's moun-tain, All gain but dross,
3. In match-less grace I can-not meas-ure, He took my place

if I but dare; 'Twill all be right, if there he need me, And
my sins to bear; Till from the cross there sprang a foun-tain To
up-on the tree; To see his face, my high-est pleas-ure, The

CHORUS.

I will fol-low an-y-where.
heal all earth-ly sin and care. Yes, I will dare to fol-low
face of him who died for me.

rit.

Je-sus, To fol-low Je-sus an-y-where, (an-y-where,) He

a tempo.

died for me on Calv'ry's tree, And I would fol-low an-y-where.

62. We'll All Get Home Some Day.

Clarence E. Flynn.

E. S. Lorenz.

1. We have a promise clear and true, On which our hope we stay, That when the toil of life is thro' We'll all get home some day.
2. Tho' long the years our hearts must wait, Tho' thorn-y be the way, We'll reach at last the shining gate; We'll all get home some day.
3. Our Father's house is built a-bove, A man-sion bright with day, A house of peace, a home of love; We'll all be there some day.
4. With courage let us onward fare; See yon-der shin-ing ray! The lights of God are gleaming there; We'll all get home some day.

CHORUS.

We'll all get home, get

We'll All Get Home Some Day.

home some blessed day! We'll all get home a-long the glo-ry way! Fight

on, keep faith, still watch and pray; Get home some day.
We'll all get home,

---

63.   **Abide With Me.**

Henry Francis Lyte.   W. H. Monk.

1. A - bide with me, fast falls the e - ven - tide; The dark-ness
2. I need thy pres - ence ev - 'ry pass - ing hour, What but thy
3. Swift to its close ebbs out life's lit - tle day; Earth's joys grow

deep - ens, Lord, with me a - bide; When oth - er help - ers
grace can foil the tempter's pow'r? Who, like thy - self, my
dim; its glo - ries pass a - way; Change and de - cay in

fail, and com - forts flee, Help of the helpless, oh, a - bide with me!
guide and stay can be? Thro' cloud and sunshine, oh, a - bide with me!
all a - round I see; O thou who chang-est not, a - bide with me!

64. To Live to Help Others.

Mattie B. Shannon.   B. D. Ackley.

1. To live to help oth - ers, may this be my pray'r; Some sor-row to les - sen, some bur - den to share; In earth's ma - ny pla - ces a task waits for me, In liv - ing for oth - ers I'll live, Lord, for thee.

2. To live to help oth - ers, shall this be my life? Thy com-fort to car - ry un - ruf - fled by strife? If serv - ice for oth - ers is done for thy sake, Thy love will help light-en the bur - den I take.

3. To live to help oth - ers, to guide them from wrong, To si - lence a sob - bing, to wak - en a song, To tell of thy par - don, thy love, and thy care, In liv - ing for oth - ers thy joy, Lord, I'll share.

CHORUS.

To live to help oth - ers from day un - to day, To live to help oth - ers, to show them thy way: To live to help oth - ers, may

To Live to Help Others.

poco rit.

this be my plea, In serv-ice for oth-ers I'll live, Lord, for thee.

65. Blessed Consolation.

F. S. Shepard.

Herm. von Berge.

1. What a bless-ed con-so-la-tion Comes to those who love the Lord,
2. There can be no path so drea-ry, But his love will cheer the way;
3. What a joy to know the Fa-ther Will not sleep or wea-ry be,

When they rest in full as-sur-ance On the prom-ise of his word.
There can be no night so gloom-y, But 'twill light-en in-to day.
But will guard our ev-'ry foot-step, E-ven tho' we can-not see.

rit.

Ev-'ry care of life will van-ish, All its shad-ows flee a-way;
There can be no cross so heav-y, But 'twill eas-y be to bear,
By his ev-er pres-ent Spir-it He will guide our feet a-right,

a tempo.

Peace will fill the soul with glad-ness, Joy will brighten ev-'ry day.
If we lean up-on his prom-ise, And but trust his love and care.
Lead-ing on-ward, lead-ing up-ward To our home in heaven's light.

66.

God is the Light.

May Justus.   Ira B. Wilson.

1. God is the light! In him no dark-ness dwell-eth;
2. God is the light! O earth in shad-ows grop-ing,
3. God is the light! Sing no more songs of sad-ness,

God is the light of heav'n and earth and sea, From age to
Look up! look up! Your night shall pass a-way! O faith-ful
Shed no more tears for sor-rows all gone by; Al-read-y

age the eyes of men he fill-eth With vi-sions of his
ones, be-yond all earth-ly hop-ing, See hope ful-filled in
see the morn-ing star of glad-ness, Al-read-y see the

CHORUS.

won-ders yet to be.
heaven's per-fect day.   God is the light, e-ter-nal in its
day-spring from on high.

rit. e cres.

glo-ry; God is the light of heav'n, and all is well.

67. I Am His Forever.

W. C. Poole.

E. S. Lorenz.

1. Oh, the joy to know, As I on-ward go, That my
2. When the way seems long, And the foe seems strong, There is
3. When my work is done, And the vic-t'ry won, And I

Lord will fail me nev-er; Thro' the dark and light, In the
One who fails me nev-er; As I walk his way To the
cross o'er Jor-dan's riv-er, This shall be my song Thro' the

path of right, I am his and his for-ev-er.
gates of day, I am his and his for-ev-er.
ag-es long, I am his and his for-ev-er.

CHORUS.

His for-ev-er, day by day! His for-ev-er, all the way!

This my song shall be thro' eter-ni-ty, I am his and his for-ev-er!

68.
Why should I Fear?

Marian Merle Bruce.

Fred. B. Holton.

1. I am dwell-ing, safe-ly dwell-ing in my Lord's se-cret place,
2. Midst the tu-mult I am cov-ered by his shel-ter-ing wings,
3. When tempta-tion would o'er-whelm me, he will nev-er for-sake,

Where no e-vil can harm me, nor hide his dear face;
Tho' the tem-pest sweep o'er me, my heart glad-ly sings;
For he knows ev-'ry need, and the way that I take;

For his pow-er will de-liv-er, my fort-ress will be,
For what-ev-er will be-fall me, his love I can see,
Till my jour-ney here is end-ed, and heav-en I see,

I rest in his good-ness, he car-eth for me.
Then why should I mur-mur, he car-eth for me.
My Sav-ior will keep me, he car-eth for me.

CHORUS.

He will hide me, hide me, why should I fear?...
He will hide me, safe-ly hide me, so why should I fear?...

Why should I Fear?

Ills ne'er be-tide me when Je-sus is near; He will guide me, guide me

He will guide me, will guide me in

his chos-en way, In him is my ref-uge for-ev-er and aye.

69. Have Thine Own Way, Lord.

Geo. O. Webster.　　　　　　　　　　　　　Ira B. Wilson.

1. Here is my heart, Lord, Make it thine own; En-ter and
2. Sav-ior and Mas-ter, Thee I a-dore, My heart is
3. Cleanse me and use me, Sav-ior di-vine, Have thine own

CHORUS.

fill it, There set thy throne.
thine, Lord, Thine ev-er-more. Take full pos-ses-sion,
way, Lord, My heart is thine.

Hum-bly I pray; Here in my heart, Lord, Have thine own way.

70. Somebody Prayed for You.

Mrs. Mary B. Wingate. E. S. Lorenz.

1. Some-bod-y prayed for you, prayed for your soul, Prayed you might walk the
2. Some-bod-y helped you by shar-ing the load, Lest you should fall, or
3. Some-bod-y cheered when your strength seemed to fail, Lest you should faint and

straight, narrow way; Some-bod-y helped you in reach-ing your goal,
faint by the way; Some-bod-y cleared all the stones from the road;
fall by the way; Some-bod-y strengthened and helped you pre-vail,

Whom are you help-ing to-day? Some-bod-y told of the love of your Lord,
Whom are you help-ing to-day? Some-bod-y guarded your innocent youth,
Whom are you cheering to-day? Some-bod-y bids you to seek for the lost,

Some-bod-y told how he'd lead in the way, Told of the truth you would
Some-bod-y warned of the snares in the way; Some-bod-y led in the
Those who are grop-ing and go-ing a-stray, Some-bod-y saved you at

find in his word, Whom are you tell-ing, are you tell-ing to-day?
path-way of truth, Whom are you lead-ing, are you guarding to-day?
in-fin-ite cost; Whom are you help-ing, are you sav-ing to-day?

Somebody Prayed for You.

CHORUS.

Are you praying for some-bod-y, pray-ing to-day? Are you work-ing for some-bod-y, work-ing al-way? Are you tell-ing the sto-ry to some-one a-stray? Are you tell-ing, are you tell-ing the old sto-ry to-day?

71. Just as I am.

Charlotte Elliott.   Wm. B. Bradbury.

1. Just as I am, with-out one plea, But that Thy blood was shed for me,
2. Just as I am, and wait-ing not To rid my soul of one dark blot,
3. Just as I am, thou wilt re-ceive, Wilt welcome, par-don, cleanse, re-lieve;
4. Just as I am, thy love un-known Has bro-ken ev-'ry bar-rier down;

And that Thou bidst me come to Thee, O Lamb of God, I come, I come.
To thee, whose blood can cleanse each spot, O Lamb of God, I come, I come.
Be-cause thy prom-ise I be-lieve, O Lamb of God, I come, I come.
Now to be thine, yea, thine a-lone, O Lamb of God, I come, I come.

72. Telling Them the King's Own Words.

May Brainerd Smith.

Herm. von Berge.

1. Mov-ing 'mid a throng who do not know His face, Meeting oft with
2. Words of in - vi - ta - tion, spo-ken by His voice, Precious words of
3. Tell the wea - ry-heart-ed of His promised rest, Tell the sor - row-
4. Tell them how He longs to wel-come ev -'ry one In His heav'n-ly

those who never knew His grace, We must be His witnesses in ev 'ry place,
promise, bidding them rejoice, Words of loving warning, calling to a choice,
lad-en of His comfort blest, Tell the tempted ones of strength when sorely pressed,
mansion when earth's race is run, Tell them of the joy of hearing His "Well done!"

CHORUS.

Telling them the King's own words. Telling, tell-ing ev-'ry-where we
Telling, tell - ing, telling ev-'ry-

go, Tell-ing, telling, He would have it so,
where we go, Tell-ing, tell - ing, for the King would have it so,

Tell-ing, tell-ing, all his love to show, Telling in the King's own words.

73. You Will Need Jesus.

Herbert Buffum.　　　　　　　　　　　　　　Ira B. Wilson.

Andante e grazioso.

1. Je - sus is knock - ing a - gain at your door, Long - ing to
2. You may not feel your great need of him now, You may care
3. Wait not till shad - ows are gath - er - ing round, Wait not till

en - ter and stay; Tho' you've re - ject - ed him man - y times o'er,
lit - tle to pray; Some time your knee in con - tri - tion will bow,
death comes your way, Lest un - pre - pared in the judgment you're found;

CHORUS.

You will need Je - sus some day. You will need him
You will need Je - sus some day. You will need him
You will need Je - sus some day. You will need Je - sus some

some day; You will need him some day; Grieve him no
day; You will need Je - sus some day;

long-er, lest he turn a - way; You will need Je - sus some day. (some day.)

74. Come Unto Me, Ye Weary.

W. C. Dix.

R. M. Stults.

Come Unto Me, Ye Weary.

O lov - ing voice of Je - sus, Which comes to cheer the night!

Our hearts were filled with sad - ness, And we had lost our way,

D. C. al Fine.

But he has brought us glad - ness, And songs at break of day.

75. Communion Hymn.

W. C. Poole.　　　　　　　　　　　　　　　B. D. Ackley.

1. Bread of life, for sin - ners bro - ken On the cross of Cal - va - ry,
2. Blood of life, so free - ly flow - ing From a Sav - ior's wounded side,
3. Life of life, O Sav - ior, ev - er May I find my life in thee!
4. Blood and body, soul and spir - it, Life of life, my all in all,

After last verse.

Sancti - fy to - day this token, Let me feed my soul on thee.
Cleanse and keep me ever knowing, I am 'neath the cleansing tide.
Keep me close and fail me never, Now and thro' e - ter - ni - ty.
Let me by thy grace in-her-it Life e - ter - nal from the fall. A - men.

76.　　O Lamb of God, I Come.

Charlotte Elliott.

E. S. Lorenz.

1. Just as I am, without one plea,
2. Just as I am, tho' tossed about,

Just as I am,............ without one plea, ... But that Thy

But that Thy blood was shed for me, And that Thou
With many a storm, with many a doubt, Fightings with-
blood .... was shed for me,..............

bidd'st me come to Thee, O Lamb of God,......... I come, I come!
in and fears without, O Lamb of God, I come, I come!

Just as I am!.... Just as I am!
Just as I am and wait-ing not.... To rid my soul of one dark blot,
Just as I am thou wilt re - ceive, Wilt welcome, pardon, cleanse, re-lieve,

To thee whose blood can cleanse each spot, O Lamb of God, I come, I come!
Because thy promise I be-lieve, O Lamb of God, I come, I come!

77. Always the Same.

Rene Bronner.

Fred B. Holton.

1. When I am wea - ry, when I am sad, When I am hap - py, when I am glad, Je - sus is with me, faith - ful and true, Ten - der and loy - al, what - ev - er I do.
2. When in the dark - ness, far in the night, Je - sus is near me, bring - ing the light, Close by me ev - er, he is my Friend, Al - ways the same, e - ven un - to the end.
3. When I am lone - ly, when I'm op - pressed, His arms are 'round me, bring - ing me rest; When deep in sor - row, sad - ness and grief, He is my com - fort, my help, and re - lief.

CHORUS.

Al - ways the same, Je - sus my own, Dear to my heart his love has grown; Al - ways the same, ev - er to be, Faith - ful thro' all e - ter - ni - ty.

78. Watch and Pray.

Fanny J. Crosby.

Ira B. Wilson.

1. Watch with Je-sus ev-'ry hour, Watch and pray, watch and pray;
2. Gen-tly speaks a voice with-in, Watch and pray, watch and pray;
3. When our faith in him is strong, Watch and pray, watch and pray;

Still a-gainst the tempter's pow'r, Watch and pray. When the skies are
When the world al-lures to sin, Watch and pray. Lest its friendship
When our hearts are full of song, Watch and pray. Cling to him, our

bright and clear, Watch and pray, watch and pray; Clouds perchance are
may de-ceive, Watch and pray, watch and pray; Lest the Sav-ior
pre-cious Guide, Watch and pray, watch and pray; Lest our feet should

CHORUS.

hov-'ring near, Watch and pray. Oh, then ev-'ry
we should grieve, Watch and pray.
turn a-side, Watch and pray. Oh, then ev-'ry

hour, Watch and pray, watch and pray; Still a-
hour, ev-'ry hour,

Watch and Pray.

gainst........ the temp-ter's pow'r   Watch and pray.
Still a-gainst

79. Lead, Kindly Light.

H. Newman.   J. B. Dykes.

1. Lead, kindly light! a-mid th'en-circling gloom,   Lead Thou me
2. I was not ev - er thus, nor pray'd that Thou Shouldst lead me
3. So long Thy pow'r hath blest me, sure it still   Will lead me

on. The night is dark and I am far from home;   Lead Thou me
on. I loved to choose and see my path; but now   Lead Thou me
on, O'er moor and fen, o'er crag and torrent, till The night is

on, Keep Thou my feet; I do not ask to see
on, I loved the gar - ish day, and, spite the fears
gone, And with the morn those an - gel fac - es smile,

The dis - tant scene; one step e - nough   for me.
Pride ruled my will; re - mem - ber not   past years.
Which I have loved long since, and lost   a - while.

81

80. I Have a Friend in Jesus.

W. C. Martin.

J. E. Delmarter.

1. I have a Friend in Je-sus, and the love he has for me Is
2. I can-not tell why Je-sus loves a poor, lost soul like me, And
3. My heart is his, in glad re-turn for his dear love to me, I

great-er than the world has ev-er known, 'Tis high-er than the
dies to pay the debt I ought to pay; Why should my Sav-ior
con-se-crate my-self to him a-lone; My joy will be to

stars a-bove, and deep-er than the sea, And last-ing as his
suf-fer to pro-vide me with a plea Which meets my needs up-
serve him till I cross the nar-row sea, Then lay my lov-ing

CHORUS.

own e-ter-nal throne.
on the judg-ment day? He loves me, yes, I know that Je-sus
heart be-fore his throne.

loves me, His cross reveals the greatness of his love; I can-not tell the

I Have a Friend in Jesus.

rit.

rea - son, but he loves me, And I am hap-py in his love.

81.

The Heart of God.

C. B. McA.

Cleland B. McAfee.

1. There is a place of qui - et rest, Near to the heart of God, A
2. There is a place of com-fort sweet, Near to the heart of God, A
3. There is a place of full re-lease, Near to the heart of God, A

place where sin can - not mo-lest, Near to the heart of God.
place where we our Sav - ior meet, Near to the heart of God.
place where all is joy and peace, Near to the heart of God.

CHORUS.

O Je - sus, blest Re-deem - er, Sent from the heart of God, Hold

us, who wait be - fore thee, Near to the heart of God.

82. When the Master Has His Way.

George O. Webster.

E. S. Lorenz.

1. Tho' life's sky be o - ver-cast, Cloud and darkness can - not last;
2. Tho' life's stormy bil - lows roll, Peace and joy may fill the soul,
3. Pow'rs of e - vil may as - sail; O - ver these we may pre - vail,

Nev - er fear, tho' dark the day; There's a gate - way to the blue,
Songs of glad-ness fill the day; How, we may not al - ways tell,
Know-ing vic - t'ry day by day; And this tri - umph we may know,

It will o - pen wide to you When the Mas-ter has his way.
But we know that all is well When the Mas-ter has his way.
O - ver-com - ing ev - 'ry foe, When the Mas-ter has his way.

CHORUS.

Pathways brighten, burdens light - en, Day by day,
lighten, Tho' the storm-clouds lower, cold and gray;

All will come out right at last, When the Master has his way.

83. He Will Never Pass You By.

Kate Wakeman Marsh.　　　　　　　　　　　　　　Ira B. Wilson.

1. Wea - ry wand'rer, will you lis - ten? 'Tis the Sav-ior draw-ing
2. Are you hun - ger - ing and thirst - ing? Christ a - lone can sat - is -
3. Then ac - cept the great sal - va - tion, For you Je - sus came to

nigh; If you're will - ing to re - ceive him, He will
fy; If you're long - ing to re - ceive him, He will
die; Then be - lieve him, oh, re - ceive him, And he'll

CHORUS.

nev - er pass you by. He will nev-er pass you by!
　　　　　　　　　　　　　　　　　nev - er pass you by!

He will nev - er pass you by! If you will
　　　nev - er pass you by!

trust him and be - lieve him, He will nev - er pass you by.

84. Like as a Father.

May M. Brewster.　　　　　　　　　　　　Ira B. Wilson.

1. Like as a fa - ther pit - i - eth his chil - dren, Lov - ing and
2. Our frame he know - eth, ev - er he re - mem - b'reth With what strange
3. Like as a fa - ther would to all his chil - dren For grief and

kind, what-ev - er may be - tide,　　E'en so the Lord doth
fires he mixed our mor - tal clay;　　He heal - eth all our
pain give sol - ace and re - lease,　　So doth the Lord in

pit-y them that fear him, He will be mer-ci-ful, nor al-ways chide.
ills, and our transgressions Far from his sight he hath re-moved a - way.
love his own re-mem-ber; Ten-der and gracious is his gift of peace.

CHORUS.

From ev - er - last - ing to ev - er - last - ing, God's

mer - cy falls wher - e'er we be; O soul, for - get not

Like as a Father.

poco rit.

his bound-less bless - ings, The Fa-ther e'er re-mem-b'reth thee.

85.

New York Observer.

Tell it to God.

Herm. von Berge.

1. What-ev - er trou - bles thee, Tell it to God, All thy anx-
2. Doth care cor - rode thy life? Tell it to God, Art wea - ry
3. Art griev-ing o'er thy loss? Tell it to God, Art sink - ing
4. Whate'er thee may be - fall, Tell it to God, Thy grief or

i - e - ty, Tell it to God! For ev - 'ry earth - ly grief
with the strife? Tell it to God! He will thy bur - dens share,
'neath the cross? Tell it to God! He can re - lieve thy pain,
great or small, Tell it to God! Trust him, he know-eth best,

This is thy sweet re - lief; Halt not in un - be - lief:
Bring him thy ev - 'ry care, And he will help thee bear:
He will with grace sus - tain, Fill thee with joy a - gain:
To him bring each re - quest, In him find peace and rest:

Tell it to God! Halt not in un - be - lief: Tell it to God.
Tell it to God! And he will help thee bear: Tell it to God.
Tell it to God! Fill thee with joy a - gain: Tell it to God.
Tell it to God! In him find peace and rest: Tell it to God.

86. When Jesus Found Me.

L. M. G.

Lottie M. Gage.

DUET. *Melody in Alto.*

1. When the sins of wast-ed life, like fet-ters bound me, In the
   tur-moil and the strife, Je-sus found me; Then his ten-der call I
   heard, And with shame my heart was stirred, Then he shed his ra-diant
   light a-round me.

2. There was strength to stand for right a-mid temp-ta - tion, When I
   knew my Master's plan of sal - va - tion; There was joy for ev-'ry
   pain, And a peace that will re - main, When with-in the dark-est
   hour he found me.

3. Tho' we wan-der down the broad high-way, un-heed - ing, We may
   hear the Sav-ior's call, gen-tly plead - ing; Know his love that conquers
   fear, Feel his pres-ence ev - er near, In the straight and nar - row
   way with Je - sus.

CHORUS.

'Twas a hap-py day when Je-sus found me, And the chains of sin no lon-ger bound me; There was joy and there was

When Jesus Found Me.

love, There was peace from God a-bove, When my Sav-ior sought and found me.

87. Follow Christ to Victory.

Mary Brainerd Smith.

Ira B. Wilson.

1. Chris-tian sol-dier, rise, Fight to win the prize. Face the foe and
2. 'Tis in faith's good fight For the truth and right Ye must bat-tle
3. With the Lead-er near, Cast a-side all fear, Press-ing for-ward

do not flee; Bid all sloth be gone, Gird your ar-mor on,
man-ful-ly; Yea, the strong-est foe Sore de-feat shall know,
val-iant-ly; Faith and hope ne'er dim, Put your trust in him,

CHORUS.

Fol-low Christ to vic-to-ry. Hear the Cap-tain's call,

Slow and emphatic.

Fol-low one and all, Fol-low Christ to vic-to-ry.

88. Be Glad for the Joys You Own.

Rene Bronner.

Herm. von Berge.

1. When life seems a des-ert of care and woe, Be glad for the joys you
2. When dark seems the way, and your feet are sore, Be glad for the joys you
3. When out on the sea, and the waves run high, Be glad for the joys you

own; When the fu-ture is dark, and the lights are low, Be
own; There are hard-er roads far you have trod be-fore; Be
own; There is One who can save, who is ev-er nigh; Be

glad for the joys you own. For this mer-ry old world swings to and fro
glad for the joys you own. For some happy old song you still can sing,
glad for the joys you own. For the sun-ny days come when storms are past;

With the joys of life you ought to know; A-wake! be-fore they fade and go:
That can make the world with gladness ring With prais-es to your heav'nly King:
Tho' the skies be dark and o-ver-cast, You'll safe-ly reach the shore at last:

Be glad for the joys you own, Be glad for the joys you own.

89. Joy Cometh in the Morning.

Mrs. Mary M. Weinland.

E. S. Lorenz.

1. Oh, wea - ry pil-grim, lift your head, For joy com-eth in the
2. Ye trembling saints, dismiss your fears, For joy com-eth in the
3. Let ev - 'ry burdened soul look up, For joy com-eth in the
4. Our God shall wipe all tears a - way, For joy com-eth in the

morn-ing; For God in his own Word hath said That joy cometh in the
morn-ing; O weep-ing mourner, dry your tears, For joy cometh in the
morn-ing; And ev - 'ry trembling sin - ner hope, For joy cometh in the
morn-ing; Sor - row and sigh-ing flee a - way, For joy cometh in the

Com-eth in the morn-ing!

CHORUS.

morn - ing. Joy com-eth in the morn - - ing!

Joy com-eth in the morn - - ing! Weep-ing may en-
Joy, joy com-eth in the morn-ing!

dure for a night, But joy com-eth in the morn - ing!

90.

Drifting Away.

J. M. B.

James M. Black.

1. Drift - ing a - way, you are drift - ing from Je - sus, Drift - ing a -
2. Drift - ing a - way from the love that redeemed you, Drift - ing a -
3. Drift - ing a - way, when you might come to Je - sus, For he is
4. O - pen the door of your heart to his mer - cy, O - pen the

way in - to sin and de - spair; Far - ther and far - ther each
way from its sun - shine and cheer; Out on the deep roll - ing
ten - der - ly call - ing to - day; While still in mer - cy his
door, for he waits to come in; His might - y arms will for -

day you are drift - ing, Drift - ing a - way from his love and his care.
bil - lows of e - vil, Out where the hopes of the soul dis - ap - pear.
arms are ex - tend-ed, And while he pleads, brother, turn not a - way.
ev - er pro-tect you, And all your heart shall be cleansed from its sin.

CHORUS.

Drift - ing a - way, Drift -
Drift - ing, drift - ing, you are drift - ing far a - way, Drift - ing,

ing a - way; While
drift - ing from the Sav - ior ev - 'ry day; While he is

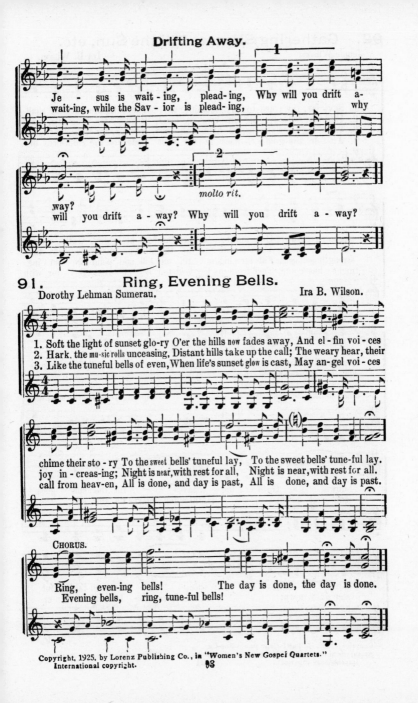

Drifting Away.

1
Je - sus is wait - ing, plead - ing, Why will you drift a - way?
wait-ing, while the Sav - ior is plead - ing, why

2
molto rit.
way?
will you drift a - way? Why will you drift a - way?

---

91. ## Ring, Evening Bells.

Dorothy Lehman Sumerau.   Ira B. Wilson.

1. Soft the light of sunset glo-ry O'er the hills now fades away, And el - fin voi - ces
2. Hark, the mu-sic rolls unceasing, Distant hills take up the call; The weary hear, their
3. Like the tuneful bells of even, When life's sunset glow is cast, May an-gel voi - ces

chime their sto - ry To the sweet bells' tuneful lay, To the sweet bells' tune-ful lay.
joy in - creas-ing; Night is near, with rest for all, Night is near, with rest for all.
call from heav-en, All is done, and day is past, All is done, and day is past.

CHORUS.

Ring, even-ing bells! The day is done, the day is done.
Evening bells, ring, tune-ful bells!

92. Gathering Sheaves Till the Sun, etc.

Jennie Wilson.   Ira B. Wilson.

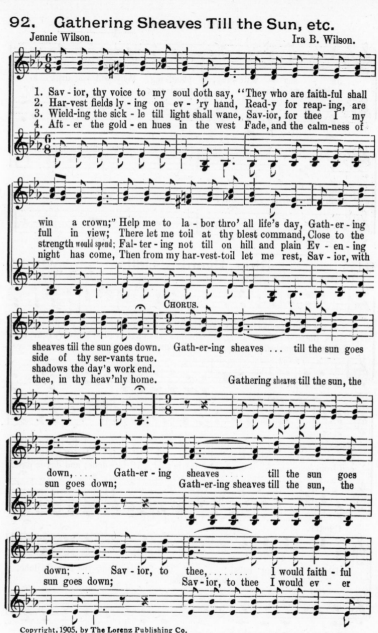

1. Sav - ior, thy voice to my soul doth say, "They who are faith-ful shall
2. Har-vest fields ly - ing on ev - 'ry hand, Read-y for reap- ing, are
3. Wield-ing the sick - le till light shall wane, Sav-ior, for thee I my
4. Aft - er the gold - en hues in the west Fade, and the calm-ness of

win a crown;" Help me to la - bor thro' all life's day, Gath-er - ing
full in view; There let me toil at thy blest command, Close to the
strength would spend; Fal - ter - ing not till on hill and plain Ev - en ing
night has come, Then from my har-vest-toil let me rest, Sav - ior, with

Chorus.

sheaves till the sun goes down. Gath-er-ing sheaves ... till the sun goes
side of thy ser-vants true.
shadows the day's work end.
thee, in thy heav'nly home.   Gathering sheaves till the sun, the

down, ... Gath-er - ing sheaves ... till the sun goes
sun goes down; Gath-er-ing sheaves till the sun, the

down; ... Sav - ior, to thee, ... I would faith - ful
sun goes down; Sav-ior, to thee I would ev - er

Gathering Sheaves Till the Sun Goes Down.

be,.... Gath-er-ing sheaves..... till the sun goes down.
faith-ful be, gath-er-ing sheaves

93. God Is Love.

Rev. A. H. Ackley.   B. D. Ackley.

1. God is light, the light of good-ness, Bright-er than the noon-day sun;
2. God is love, the love that gave us Je-sus Christ, the sin-ner's Friend;
3. God is spir-it, pure and ho-ly, He knows ev-'ry-thing we do;

Light that saves and heals and sweetens, Light that bless-es ev-'ry-one.
Love that nev-er, nev-er chang-es, Love for-ev-er with-out end.
When we pray in truth and spir-it, He will hear and an-swer, too.

CHORUS.

God is light, God is love, God is spir-it from a-bove;

Wor-ship him in truth and spir-it, God is light, God is love.

94. Walk Closer to Jesus.

W. C. Poole.　　　　　　　　　　　　　　　　　E. S. Lorenz.

1. When the way is long, And the foe is strong, When the lights that shine grow dim;
2. When you are alone, And the Father's throne Seems so far you scarce can pray;
3. When the shadows fall, And the voices call, And the lights of earth grow dim;

Like a star so bright In the dark of night There is One; walk close to Him.
There is One so near, With His light to cheer, As he plans and leads thy way.
He will light the way To the gates of day, Where he reigns; go walk with him.

CHORUS.

Walk clos-er to Je-sus—each step of the way, Walk clos-er to Je-sus— if dark is the day; Walk clos-er to Je-sus— if light should grow dim, Thy way he will brighten—walk clos-er to him.

95. The Unseen Hand.

Myrtle B. Lewis. Herm. von Berge.

1. When the morn of life is glowing With its glo-ry in the skies,
2. When in earn-est toil I wres-tle With the du-ties of the day,
3. When at last the shad-ows lengthen And the eve of day is come,

When the path my feet must wander Strewn with flow'rs before me lies,
When thro' life's en-tan-gled maz-es Oft I can-not find my way;
When the wand'rer, spent and weary, Longs for rest and longs for home;

When be-fore life's un-tried dan-gers In the zeal of youth I
When the house that I had build-ed Seems to rest on sink-ing
When his list'ning ears seem catch-ing Ech-oes from the gold-en

stand, There is One who watch-es o'er me, Guid-ing
sand, Thro' my tri-als and my fail-ures Gen-tly
strand, There will guide him thro' the por-tals Still the

by the un-seen hand, Guid-ing by the un-seen hand.
leads the un-seen hand, Gen-tly leads the un-seen hand.
lov-ing, un-seen hand, Still the lov-ing, un-seen hand.

96. Take Your Troubles To Jesus.

James Rowe.　　　　　　　　　　　　　　　　　Herm. von Berge.

1. Why let life be drear-y when it may be bright? Why be
2. Why be go - ing downward, when you ought to climb? Why be
3. You have gathered thorns in-stead of ros - es fair, And in-

al-ways struggling in a los - ing fight? Have a Friend be - side you
sad when joy-bells ought to peal and chime? Get in touch with Christ and
stead of gladness you have won de-spair; Leave the path you fol - low,

who will keep things right: Take your troub-les all to Je - sus.
have a hap - py time: Take your troub-les all to Je - sus.
on - ly gloom is there; Take your troub-les all to Je - sus.

CHORUS.

Take your troub-les all to Je - sus! Take your
Are you wea - ried as you walk a - long your way?

trou - bles all to Je - sus! Have a
Come, your troub-les all at Je - sus' feet to lay!

Take Your Troubles to Jesus.

Friend be-side you who will keep and guide you: Take your troubles all to Je - sus.

97. ## My Jesus, I Love Thee.

London Hymn Book.   Arr. from Thomas Koschat.

1. My Je - sus, I love thee, I know thou art mine, For
2. I love thee be - cause thou hast first lov - ed me, And
3. I'll love thee in life, I will love thee in death, And
4. In man-sions of glo - ry and end - less de - light, I'll

thee all the fol - lies of sin I re - sign; My gra-cious Re-
purchased my par - don on Cal-va-ry's tree; I love thee for
praise thee as long as thou lend-est me breath; And say when the
ev - er a - dore thee in heav-en so bright; I'll sing with the

deem - er, my Sav - ior art thou, If ev - er I loved thee, my
wear - ing the thorns on thy brow, If ev - er I loved thee, my
death-dew lies cold on my brow, If ev - er I loved thee, my
glit - ter - ing crown on my brow, If ev - er I loved thee, my

Je - sus, 'tis now! If ev - er I loved thee, my Je - sus, 'tis now.

98. Go, Tell the World.

Calia Altstaetter　　　　　　　　　　　　　　　　　　Ira B. Wilson.

1. Go, tell the world a-bout Je - sus, Go and love's message un- fold,
2. Go, tell the world a-bout Je - sus, Till all the message have heard,
3. Go, tell the world a-bout Je - sus, Go spread his gos- pel of love,

Strangest, most beau-ti-ful sto - ry　Ev - er to mor- tal was told.
Tell of the prom-is-es　pre - cious　Found in his own bless-ed word;
It　is the hope of the na - tions, Love our sal - va-tion will prove.

Tell how he came down from heav - en That we re-demp-tion might know,
It will bring rest to the wea - ry, Hope to the poor and op - pressed,
Tell all the na-tions and peo - ples Ev - 'ry-where un - der the sun,

Tell it, ye Christians who've proved it, Tell it wher-ev- er you　go.
Peace to the anx-ious and troub-led, Thro' him all na-tions are　blest.
Till ev-'ry heart shall ac-cept him, Till all the world has been won.

CHORUS.

Go,　　tell a - bout Je - sus, Love's　mes-sage un - fold;
Go, tell the world a- bout Je - sus, Go, and love's message un- fold;

Go, Tell the World.

rit.

Strang-est, most beau-ti-ful sto - ry Ev - er to mor-tal was told.

99.   We Go This Way But Once.

British Weekly.   E. S. Lorenz.

1. We go this way but once,   O heart of mine,
2. We go this way but once!   Ah, nev - er - more
3. We go this way but once! (but once,) Then let us make

So why not make the jour - ney well worth while? Giv-ing to those who
Can we go back a - long the self - same way To get more out of
The road we trav - el blos - som - y and sweet With helpful, kindly,

trav - el on, who trav - - el on,   A
life and seek to stem   the wrong,   Or
lov - ing deeds and cheer - - ing words,   To

1. Giv - ing to those who trav - el on,
2. To seek to stem, to stem the wrong,
3. With kind-ly deeds and cheer - ing words

help - ing hand, a word of cheer, a kind - ly smile?
speak love's words we knew, but strange-ly did   not say.
smooth the path, the path of bruised and stum - bling feet.

100. A Present Help is He.

John G. Whittier.   E. S. Lorenz.

1. We may not climb the heav'nly steeps To bring the Lord Christ down;
2. The heal-ing of the seamless dress Is by our beds of pain;

In vain we search the lowest deeps, For him no depths can drown.
We touch him in life's storm and stress, And we are whole a - gain.

But warm, sweet, tender, ev - en yet A pres - ent help is he;
Thro' him the first fond pray'rs are said, Our lips of childhood frame;

And faith has yet its Ol - i - vet, And love its Gal - i - lee.
The last low whis - pers of our dead Are burdened with his name.

CODA.

O Lord and Mas-ter of us all, What-e'er our name or sign,

A Present Help Is He.

We own thy sway, we heed thy call, We test our lives by thine.

101.　　　There Is No Other Way.

T. O. Chisholm.

B. D. Ackley.

1. "The soul that sin-neth, it shall die," Where can we suc-cor find?
2. Then where is hope for all our race, Condemned, for sin to die?
3. The an-swer see on yon-der cross, Where One was lift-ed up!
4. For God so loved this sin-ful world,—He loved us, ev-'ry one,—

For none is right-eous, no, not one, Not one, of all man-kind.
Is there no mer-cy to be found? No God to jus-ti-fy?
He bore the pen-al-ty for all, He drank the bit-ter cup.
That we might have e-ter-nal life Thro' Je-sus Christ, his Son.

CHORUS.

Oh, yes, there is a way For souls in sin a-stray,
Oh, yes, there is a way

The way that leads to Cal-va-ry; There is no oth-er way.

102. The God Who Answers Prayer.

Eben E. Rexford.   R. L. Stuckey.

1. When we're bowed with heav-y bur - dens We must car-ry day by day,
2. When the star - less night of sor - row Set-tles down up-on our way,
3. Oh,   the tho't that God will lis - ten To the pray'rs we lift to him!

Plod-ding on with wea - ry foot - step, Al-most fainting by the   way:
When the arm of flesh we trust - ed Fails to help in our dis - may:
It   is full of sweet-est com - fort When the eyes with tears grow dim.

There is One our load to light - en And our cross with us to share,
Then to know our heav'nly Fa - ther Is   a - bout us ev - 'ry-where,
Oh, to know that, of our tri - als He is nev - er un - a - ware,

If we come to Him be - liev-ing,   He will hear and an - swer pray'r.
And his ears are ev - er o - pen, If we come to him in   pray'r.
And that he will sure-ly show us That he hears and an-swers pray'r.

CHORUS.

Let us bring   un - to Him Ev-'ry bur - den,
Let us bring   un - to Him

The God Who Answers Prayer.

ev-'ry care! If up - on Him we call, He will hear and an-swer pray'r.

103.

Were You There?

With much expression.

Negro melody. Arr. by Ira B. Wilson.

1. Were you there when they cru - ci - fied my Lord? (Were you there?)
2. Were you there when they nailed him to the tree? (Were you there?)
3. Were you there when they pierced him in the side? (Were you there?)
4. Were you there when the sun re-fused to shine? (Were you there?)
5. Were you there when they laid him in the tomb? (Were you there?)

Were you there when they cru - ci - fied my Lord? (Were you there?)
Were you there when they nailed him to the tree? (Were you there?)
Were you there when they pierced him in the side? (Were you there?)
Were you there when the sun re-fused to shine? (Were you there?)
Were you there when they laid him in the tomb? (Were you there?)

Oh, some-times it caus - es me to trem-ble, trem-ble, trem-ble;

mf *Slower.* *dim-e-rit.* *p* *pp*

Were you there when they cru - ci - fied my Lord? (Were you there?)
nailed him, etc.

104. Send the News To-day.

W. C. Poole.　　　　　　　　　　　　　　　Fred B. Holton.

1. Where the mul-ti-tudes are wait-ing For the gos-pel sto-ry true,
2. Where the mil-lions now are fall-ing In the dark-ness and the night,
3. While the an-gels watch a-bove you, Wait-ing with their harps and song,

Will you help to send the mes-sage? They are wait-ing now for you;
Will you an-swer to their call-ing For the bless-ed gos-pel light?
For the bless-ed fi-nal ti-dings, "Right has triumphed o-ver wrong!"

They are call-ing for the gos-pel That will bright-en all their way,
Will you help to take the sto-ry Of sal-va-tion far a-way?
While the One who died to save you Waits your an-swer, will you say,

Will you help to send the sto-ry All a-round the world to-day?
Will you help to send the ti-dings All a-round the world to-day?
I will help to send His mes-sage All a-round the world to-day?

CHORUS.

Send the news to-day, send the news to-day, On with the

Send the News To-day.

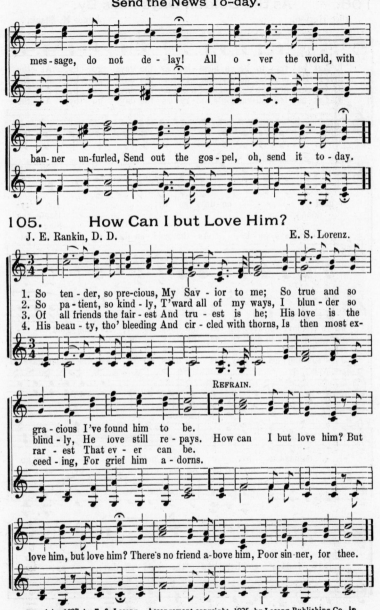

mes - sage, do not de - lay! All o - ver the world, with

ban - ner un-furled, Send out the gos - pel, oh, send it to - day.

105. How Can I but Love Him?

J. E. Rankin, D. D. E. S. Lorenz.

1. So ten - der, so pre-cious, My Sav - ior to me; So true and so
2. So pa - tient, so kind - ly, T'ward all of my ways, I blun - der so
3. Of all friends the fair - est And tru - est is he; His love is the
4. His beau - ty, tho' bleeding And cir - cled with thorns, Is then most ex-

REFRAIN.

gra - cious I've found him to be.
blind - ly, He love still re - pays. How can I but love him? But
rar - est That ev - er can be.
ceed - ing, For grief him a - dorns.

love him, but love him? There's no friend a-bove him, Poor sin - ner, for thee.

106. As the Golden Days Pass By.

Alice Horton.   James M. Black.

1. Let us try to be a bless-ing as the days go by, As the gold — — en days go by; Ev - 'ry-where His love con-fess-ing as the days go by, As the gold — — en days go by. As the gold — — en days go
2. In His serv-ice do not tar - ry as the days go by, As the Haste, the glad, good news to car - ry as the days go by,
3. We may dry the tears of sad-ness as the days go by, As the Sing - ing songs of joy and glad-ness as the days go by,
4. Let us tell sal-va-tion's sto - ry as the days go by, As the Jesus and his glo - ry as the days go by, As the golden days go by, the gold - en days go by. As the gold-en days go by, as the

golden days go by, As the gold-en days go by; Tell of

CHORUS.

As the gold — — en days go by, As the gold — — en days go by, As the gold - en days go by, As the gold-en days, as the

As the Golden Days Pass By.

by; There are heav - y hearts to light - en, Man - y
gold-en days go by;

wrongs that we may right - en, As the gold - en days go by.

107. ## My Comfort.

Rev. Howard Haven McGaughey. Ira B. Wilson.

1. The night is dark, I can - not see my way; The
2. The night is dark, I can - not see my way; The

clouds hang low, The sky is bleak and gray. The storm is great, and
clouds hang low, The sky is bleak and gray. The storm is great, but

hope a thing un-known, Despair enthroned, and I am all a - lone.
hope is not un-known; Christ is enthroned, and I am not a - lone.

108. Sweet Story of Old.

Mrs. Jemima Luke.

Norman Lighthill.

1. I think, when I read that sweet sto - ry of old, When Je - sus was
2. Yet still to his foot-stool in pray'r I may go, And ask for a

here a - mong men, How he called lit - tle chil - dren as
share in his love; And if I thus earn - est - ly

lambs to his fold, I should like to have been with him then.
seek him be - low, I shall see him and hear him a - bove,

I wish that his hands had been placed on my head, His arms had been
In that beau-ti - ful place he has gone to pre-pare For all who are

thrown a - round me;.... That I might have seen his kind
washed and for - giv'n;... And man - y dear chil - dren are

Sweet Story of Old.

look when he said, "Let the lit - tle ones come un - to me."
gath - er - ing there, "For of such is the king - dom of heav'n."

109. **A Chain of Love.**

Mattie B. Shannon.

Fred B. Holton.

1. Time can-not weaken the chain I wear, Its links were fashioned with love so rare,
2. What tho' my footsteps afar may roam, That bond, so tender, will lead me home,

rit. *molto rit.*

Bind-ing my heart for-e'er to thine, Dear mother, moth - er of mine!
Drawing me close, a chain di-vine, Dear mother, moth - er of mine!

CHORUS. *a tempo.*

A gift to me from heav'n a-bove, A wondrous chain of moth-er love!

I glad - ly wear its links so fair, A beau-ti-ful chain of love!

110. The Easter Story.

Harriet H. Pierson.

Ira B. Wilson.

1. Once a-gain the world re-joic - es At the dawn of Eas-ter-tide; Earth with
2. Once a-gain the sun - lit fount-ains Fall in drops of rainbow hue, And the
3. Once a-gain to hearts that sorrow, To the sad and heav-y- eyed, Comes a

all her my-riad voi - ces Sends her mes-sage far and wide; Ev-'ry
spring has clothed the mountains With a beau - ty ev - er new; Ev-'ry
prom- ise of the mor - row, God's e-ter - nal Eas- ter - tide; All the

blade of grass up-spring-ing, Ev-'ry bird its car - ol sing - ing, Tells the
ti - ny flow-er blow - ing, Ev-'ry brook-let swift-ly flow - ing, Tells the
earth to life a - wak - ing, From the bonds of win-ter break-ing, Tells the

sto-ry of the blessed Easter morn. (Eas-ter morn.) Hail, glad morning! The

CHORUS.

night of death is o'er; With thy dawn-ing, life o-pens wide the door;

The Easter Story.

Tell to all the world the sto-ry Of the res-ur-rec-tion glo-ry, Of the Lord who rose tri-umph-ant o-ver death for-ev-er-more.

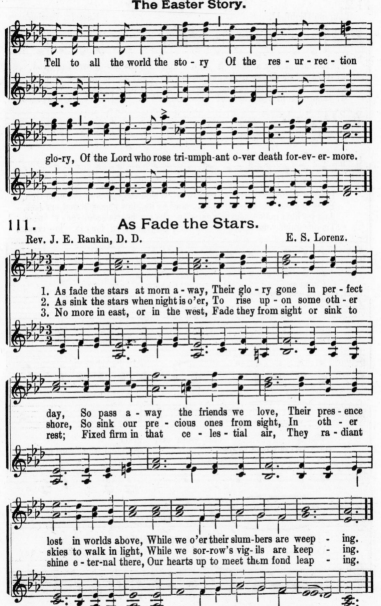

111.

As Fade the Stars.

Rev. J. E. Rankin, D. D.

E. S. Lorenz.

1. As fade the stars at morn a-way, Their glo-ry gone in per-fect day, So pass a-way the friends we love, Their pres-ence lost in worlds above, While we o'er their slum-bers are weep-ing.

2. As sink the stars when night is o'er, To rise up-on some oth-er shore, So sink our pre-cious ones from sight, In oth-er skies to walk in light, While we sor-row's vig-ils are keep-ing.

3. No more in east, or in the west, Fade they from sight or sink to rest; Fixed firm in that ce-les-tial air, They ra-diant shine e-ter-nal there, Our hearts up to meet them fond leap-ing.

112. Light is Shining

Laurene Highfield.

Eura L. Tussing.

1. 'Round our way a light is shin - ing, 'Tis the ho - ly word of God,
2. Clear it shows the rocks and pit - falls That up - on the way we meet;
3. As we read its sa - cred pag - es, 'Tis the voice of God we hear;
4. Shin - ing like a ray of bless - ing, Full of joy, and hope, and peace,

Like a lamp up - on the path-way, Which the saints of old once trod.
Bring-ing out the saf - est pla - ces, As its glow shines 'round our feet.
And its light makes heaven's glo - ry To our hearts seem ver - y near.
'Tis our guide, our rule, our com-fort, May our love for it in - crease.

CHORUS.

Pre - cious, ho - ly Bi - ble,
Pre-cious is the ho - ly Bi - ble, and we love it,

Words . . . . of truth and grace,
With its sa - cred words of truth and won-drous grace,

Point - - ing out the path - way
Point-ing out to us the saf - est, sur - est path - way

Light is Shining.

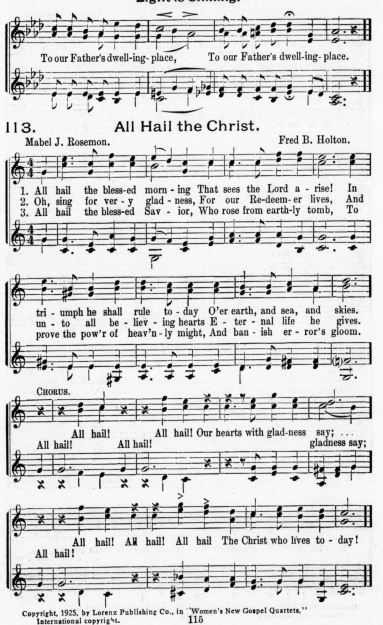

To our Father's dwell-ing- place,   To our Father's dwell-ing- place.

113. ## All Hail the Christ.

Mabel J. Rosemon.   Fred B. Holton.

1. All hail the bless-ed morn-ing That sees the Lord a - rise! In
2. Oh, sing for ver - y glad-ness, For our Re-deem- er lives, And
3. All hail the bless-ed Sav- ior, Who rose from earth-ly tomb, To

tri - umph he shall rule to - day O'er earth, and sea, and skies.
un - to all be - liev-ing hearts E - ter - nal life he gives.
prove the pow'r of heav'n - ly might, And ban - ish er - ror's gloom.

Chorus.

All hail!   All hail! Our hearts with glad-ness say; ...
All hail!   All hail!   gladness say;

All hail! All hail! All hail The Christ who lives to - day!
All hail!

114.

The Story of Jesus.

Mrs. D. Ray Campbell.

Norman Lighthill.

Alto Solo.

1. There's a sto-ry, no mat-ter how oft-en 'tis told, Ne'er los-es its
2. For in ten-der-est pit-y he looks from a-bove, With hands torn and
3. Oh, my soul, hear the sto-ry, look on him and live, For life more a-

sweet-ness, nor yet grow-eth old; It tells how the Sav-ior came
bleed-ing, great proof of his love, And shows you his wounds, say-ing,
bun-dant he glad-ly will give; Call on him for mer-cy while

seek-ing to save A world lost in sin-ning, from death and the grave.
"Child, 'twas for thee I suf-fered and bled up-on Cal-va-ry's tree."
yet it is day, Thy sins he will par-don and wash them a-way.

CHORUS.

Hear the sto-ry of Je-sus, so ten-der and true, Hear the sto-ry, oh,

Hear the

The Story of Jesus.

hear it, I pray;.... For he's of-fer-ing life ev-er-
sto-ry, oh, hear it, I pray;

rit.

last-ing to you, If you'll on-ly be-lieve him to-day...

115. Worship the King.

Sir Robert Grant.   F. J. Haydn.

1. Oh, wor-ship the King, all-glo-rious a-bove, And grate-ful-ly
2. Thy boun-ti-ful care, what tongue can re-cite? It breathes in the
3. Frail chil-dren of dust, and fee-ble as frail, In thee do we
4. Our Fa-ther and God, how faith-ful thy love! While an-gels de-

sing his won-der-ful love. Our Shield and De-fend-er, the
air, it shines in the light; It streams from the hills, it de-
trust, nor find thee to fail; Thy mer-cies, how ten-der! how
light to hymn thee a-bove, The hum-bler cre-a-tion, how

An-cient of days, Pa-vil-ioned in splen-dor and gird-ed with praise.
scends to the plain, And sweet-ly dis-tils in the dew and the rain.
firm to the end, Our Mak-er, De-fend-er, Re-deem-er and Friend!
fee-ble their lays, With true ad-o-ra-tion shall lisp to thy praise.

117

116.
Christmas Lullaby.

Charlotte G. Homer.
1st and 2nd Sopranos.

Chas. H. Gabriel.
Arranged by Ira B. Wilson.

1. Low in a manger, A dear lit-tle strang-er The bless-ed Lord Je-sus once lay; An-gels un-num-bered Kept watch while he slum-ber'd That night in his cra-dle of hay. Night-winds with sigh-ing, And na-ture re-ply-ing, U-ni-ted the Ba-by to greet;

2. Angels from glo-ry Came tell-ing the sto-ry That Je-sus, the Sav-ior, was born; Shep-herds re-ceiv-ing The word and be-liev-ing, Came seek-ing the Ba-by that morn. There when they found him, A-kneel-ing a-round him, They wor-shipp'd in awe at his feet;

Christmas Lullaby.

Hum.............

Sang to the Strang-er, A-sleep in the man-ger, A
Dear lit-tle Strang-er, A-sleep in the man-ger, So

Hum.............

Hum.............

Hum............. Rock-a-by,... dear lit-tle Strang-er,

lull-a-by si-lent and sweet. Dear lit-tle Stranger, rock-a-by-by,
in-no-cent, low-ly and sweet. Rock-a-by,... dear lit-tle Strang-er,

Hum.............

Rock-a-by, born in a man-ger, Rock-a-by,...

Born in a man-ger, by-o-by-by, An-gels a-bove thee,
Rock-a-by,.... born in a man-ger, Rock-a-by,....

an-gels a-bove thee, Rock-a-by, by-o-by.

rock-a-by-by, Hov-ered a-bove thee, by-o-by-by.
an-gels a-bove thee, Rock-a-by, by-o-by.

117.

Crossing the Bar.

Alfred Tennyson.

Ira B. Wilson.

p *Moderato.*

Sun-set and even-ing star, And one clear call for me, And may there be no moan-ing of the bar, When I put out to sea, When I put out to sea; But such a tide as mov-ing seems a-sleep, Too full for sound or foam, When that which drew from out the boundless deep Turns a - gain home. Twi-light,

Turns a - gain home. *pp* Twi-light and evening

Crossing the Bar.

even-ing bell, Even - ing bell; And may there be no sad - ness
bell, *p* And aft - er that the dark;

of fare-well When I em - bark. For tho' from out our bourne of

time and place, The flood may bear me far, I hope to see my

Pi - lot face to face, I hope to see my Pi - lot face to face,

When I have crossed the bar, When I have crossed the bar.

Rock of Ages.

A. M. Toplady.   W. S. Martin.

Andante. ♩ = 78.

Rock of Ages.

hand I bring, Sim-ply   to   thy cross I cling.
bring,   Sim-ply to   thy   cross I cling.

While I draw   this fleet-ing breath,   When mine
While I draw this   fleet-ing breath,

eye - lids close in death,   When I soar to worlds un-
When mine eye - lids   close in death,

known, See thee on thy judg-ment throne,   Rock of A - ges,
Rock of A   -   ges, cleft for

cleft for   me, Let me hide   my - self   in   thee.
me,   Let me hide my - self   in   thee.

119. **I Sleep, but Love Still Waketh.**

(For Memorial or Funeral Occasions.)

Wilbur Fisk Tillett.   Ira B. Wilson.

1. I sleep, but love still wak-eth To turn the night to day;
2. I sleep, but love still wak-eth, And lo, the ten-der care
3. I sleep, but be not griev-ing When for a time we part;

No leave the heart e'er tak-eth: Love can-not pass a-way.
Of Him who nev-er sleep-eth Is 'round us ev-'ry-where.
For, tho' I go, I'm leav-ing Be-hind my lov-ing heart.

How-ev-er deep the sleep-ing To loved ones may ap-pear,
In wak-ing or in sleep-ing No ill can e'er be-fall
'Tis not a fi-nal rend-ing Of sa-cred bonds in twain;

1st and 2nd verses. *rit.*

There is no need for weep-ing, My heart, my love is here.
Be-neath His care and keep-ing Who watch-es o-ver all.

3rd verse.   *p*   *f rit.*

For love there is no end-ing; Some day we shall meet a-gain.

120.

Guide Me!

William Williams.

Herm. von Berge.

Guide me! Guide me! Guide me, O Thou great Je-ho-vah!
Guide me, oh, guide me, Thou great Je-ho-vah, Pil-grim

Guide me! Guide me, Pil-grim thro' this bar-ren land. I am
thro' this bar-ren land, This bar-ren land.

weak, but thou art might-y, Hold me with thy pow'r-ful
I am weak, but thou art mighty, Hold me with thy

hand; Bread of heav-en, Bread of heav-en, Feed me
pow'r-ful hand;

rit.

till I want no more, Feed me till I want no more.
Till I want.... no more.

Guide Me!

a tempo.

O-pen now the crystal fount-ain, Whence the liv - ing wa-ters flow; Let the

fier - y, cloud-y pil - lar Lead me all my 'our - ney thro', Lead me
Let the fier - y   pil - lar   my

all my jour-ney thro'. Strong De - liv -'rer, Strong De - liv -'rer, Be thou
jour - ney thro'.   Strong   De - liv -'rer, Be my

still my strength and shield, Be thou still my strength and shield.
strength   and   shield,

Guide me!   Guide me!   Guide me, O thou great Je - ho - vah!
Guide me, oh, guide me, Thou great   Je - ho - vah, Pil-grim

Guide Me!

Guide me! Guide me, Pil-grim thro' this bar-ren land!
thro' this bar-ren land, This bar-ren land!

Slow and emphatic.

Guide me, guide me, Safe-ly guide me; Hold me with thy pow'r-ful hand.

Melody of "Zion," by Thos. Hasting, in 1st Alto.

Guide me! Guide me! Bid my fears.. sub-side;
When I tread the verge of Jor-dan, Bid my anxious fears sub-side; Bear me

Guide me! Guide me Thro' the swell-ing tide! Songs of praises I will
thro' the swelling current, Land me safe on Canaan's side!

ev-er give to thee; Songs of praises I will ev-er give to thee. A-men.